LOVEPATH INTERNATIONAL, INC.

Joe Beam with Rebecca Kennedy

The Path to Soul Satisfying Love Small Group Workbook

LOVEPATH INTERNATIONAL, INC.

The Path to Soul Satisfying Love
SMALL GROUP WORKBOOK

© 2011 Joe Beam

LovePath International, Inc.
330 Mallory Station Road, Suite 19
Franklin, TN 37067
Phone 866.903.0990 • Email info@JoeBeam.com

TABLE OF CONTENTS

Chapter 1 – What is Love?

Understanding the love that you have...

Love is patient, love is kind. It does not envy, it does not boast, it is not proud. It is not rude, it is not self-seeking, it is not easily angered, it keeps no record of wrongs. Love does not delight in evil but rejoices with the truth. It always protects, always trusts, always hopes, always perseveres. Love never fails. But where there are prophecies, they will cease; where there are tongues, they will be stilled; where there is knowledge, it will pass away. (1 Corinthians 13:4-8)

This workbook accompanies the *Your LovePath* book and the *Your LovePath* DVD shown in your class or group.

If you are not in a relationship, the Biblical teaching in this chapter applies to you, but the surveys do not apply now. They will, however, be very handy when you follow the LovePath to have a significant love in your life.

The Way to Use This Workbook

Each chapter of the workbook coincides with the corresponding chapter in the *Your LovePath* book and the *Your LovePath* DVD. We designed each chapter to build on the chapter before it. Before doing the exercises in this workbook, we strongly recommend that you first read the relevant chapter in the book.

Please study the Biblical introduction to each chapter of the workbook. Your leader will decide how to use that section in the limited time you have for your Bible class.

Biblical Views of Love

The New Testament was written primarily in Koine Greek language. Differing from Classical Greek, you might call it "the Greek of the street" – the language of the common person. For our consideration in this study, we refer to four distinct Koine words that refer to love. Because the Greek language may employ many variations of a word – some nouns used as verbs, differing prefixes and suffixes for specific reasons, etc. – we use only the primary word rather than listing the variations that occur in some passages.

The New Testament uses two of these words in the positive sense.

1. *agape* – It sometimes refers to a decision to do best for another person, even if you do not want to do it. (Matthew 5:44, 1 John 3:16) Sometimes it connotes unconditional caring for another

person, even when that person does not deserve it. (1 John 4:16, Romans 5:8) In essence, it is self-sacrificing love.

2. *philia* – It refers to friendship (James 4:4) and genuinely caring for another person. In John 21:14-17, Jesus twice asked Peter if he felt *agape* for Him. Each time Peter replied that he had *philia* for Him. Then Jesus asked Peter if he had *philia* for Him. Peter replied strongly that he did. With that repeated affirmation of Peter's friendship and caring love for Jesus, the Lord told him to feed His sheep.

It uses one word in the negative sense, but we understand the positive by that usage.

3. *storge* – It means natural affection, such as that of a mother for her child. In the New Testament we find it only in its negative form. The King James Version and the American Standard Version translate the negative form as "without natural affection" (Romans 1:31, 2 Timothy 3:3). Some Bible versions translate it as heartless, unloving, or inhuman.

The last word is not used in the New Testament, but is a part of Koine that becomes valid to this study because the Hebrew word for love in the Old Testament sometimes carries the same meaning.

4. *eros* – In short, *eros* means passion, "the love between and man and a woman which embraces longing, craving, and desire." (John Bisagno, *Love is Something You Do*) It is romance or being "in love." (C. S. Lewis, *The Four Loves*)

   o Some Biblical scholars ignore this word because they do not find it in the New Testament. However, the Old Testament uses this word for love – *ahav* (verb) and *ahava* (noun). God makes it clear in the Old Testament that love includes the meaning of *eros*.

      ▪ *"Come, let us take our fill of love until the morning: let us solace ourselves with love."* (Proverbs 7:18, King James Version)

      ▪ *"Come, let's drink deep of love till morning; let's enjoy ourselves with love!"* (Proverbs 7:18, New International Version)

   o Notice the use of the word "love" twice in that passage. The first is the Hebrew word that means "to boil," while the second is the Hebrew word referenced above. There is no doubt that this refers to intense sexual loving. In the Greek version of the Old Testament known as the Septuagint, the word used in this passage is *eroti*.

   o God recognizes this type of love. Therefore, we use in this study the Koine word *eros* to often refer to a romantic love and, sometimes, pure passion. In one context it may be wonderful; in the other, it may be destructive. Why? Of the four loves, it is the most self-serving, even when focused on a lover.

In our study, we show you a path to *eros*, in the best use of the word, as well as *agape*, *philia*, and *storge*. While they may occur on their own with specific circumstances – particularly *storge* when parents welcome a newborn – our concern in this study is to show the path to make each of these grow as they should. We call it the LovePath.

A Survey for Each of You

Rather than asking you to write your thoughts or share them verbally at the beginning, we provide a profile for each of you to complete. We provide a graph to plot your score. In a later chapter in the workbook, we ask you to complete the questions again to give you greater insight into your relationship.

THE SURVEY

The following three questions are from the Kansas Marital Satisfaction Survey. It was designed for married couples, but you may use it for a different relationship. If you are in a relationship but not yet married, replace "marriage" with "relationship" and "spouse" with either "fiancé," "boyfriend," or "girlfriend." To avoid constructing awkward sentences, we use the word "marriage" even if the couple is not yet married. Similarly, we use "spouse" to refer to all relationships including fiancé, boyfriend, or girlfriend. It will be up to you to make the mental adjustment for your situation.

Note that we designed this workbook and church class for heterosexual marriages legalized by governmental and Biblical standards.

Answer each question on a scale of 1 to 7.

> 1 = extremely dissatisfied
> 2 = very dissatisfied
> 3 = somewhat dissatisfied
> 4 = mixed
> 5 = somewhat satisfied
> 6 = very satisfied
> 7 = extremely satisfied

1. _____ How satisfied are you with your marriage?

2. _____ How satisfied are you with your relationship with your spouse?

3. _____ How satisfied are you with your husband/wife as a spouse?

Now add the three scores and divide by three to get an average score. _____

On the following graph, circle the number that is your average score. In a later chapter, we will show you how to plot both your average score and your partner's average score. That will provide you a snapshot of your relationship that may be quite interesting.

You dissatisfied___1_____2_____3_____4_____5_____6_____7__You Satisfied

Anything less than a four means your relationship is not to your satisfaction. A four means you are unsure about your relationship. We feel the only scores that indicate a person is happy in the relationship are either a six or seven.

Do not panic if your score is not currently a six or seven. Learning the LovePath will make a difference if each of you follows it. We have seen it work miracles in relationships that seemed to have no chance of surviving, much less thriving. We have even seen it lead people to marry again after as much as ten years of divorce.

If it can do that for those couples, it can and will lead you to a higher satisfaction score if you practice the principles of the LovePath. Even if you scored a seven, the LovePath can show you how to make your relationship deeper and more meaningful.

Moving On

Completing the short survey is crucial to what you will do in future chapters. If you wait until then to complete the surveys, you answers will be invalid. Therefore, if you want the most from this workbook – and are in a marriage or serious relationship – make sure that you have completed every question.

After the next section **Daily Thoughts and Prayers** are questions that you need to answer before coming to the next class session. Please make sure you write your answers to those before coming to class.

In the Daily Thoughts and Prayers you will find great personal growth by taking a few minutes every day to meditate and write your thoughts. Then, pray. Pray with your heart, soul, and mind. Do it every day and watch God work in you and in your relationships.

Daily Thoughts and Prayers

Day One
Spend a few minutes meditating about agape love. Jot your thoughts here.

The one thing that I will make sure I pray about today that will help me love more is....

Day Two
Spend a few minutes meditating about philia love. Jot your thoughts here.

The one thing that I will make sure I pray about today that will help me love more is....

Day Three
Spend a few minutes meditating about eros love. Jot your thoughts here.

The one thing that I will make sure I pray about today that will help me love more is….

Day Four
If you are in love, spend a few minutes remembering the "why's and what's" of your falling in love. Jot your thoughts here.

The one thing that I will make sure I pray about today that will help me love more is….

Day Five

Meditate today about what you love about yourself—not arrogantly or in vain—but in true evaluation of self. Jot your thoughts here.

The one thing that I will make sure I pray about today that will help me love more is....

Class Sharing Time

In your next group meeting, you will spend a few minutes sharing with your group. Before coming to class, think these through and write your answers. What we think and write about has dramatically more effect on us than what we talk about. Write your answers so that you get the most from this study.

- Describe what you feel would be the ideal love relationship between a man and a woman?

- What do you wish to gain from this study?

- What demonstrates to you that you are loved as you wish to be loved?

- Of the four types of love discussed in this chapter – agape, philia, storge, eros – which is the most important to you at this time in your life? Why?

- If you were to give the love that you wish to receive, what would you do differently?

Notes as you watch the DVD

Chapter 2 – Attraction

Understanding what is attractive about you...

"Who is this that appears like the dawn, fair as the moon, bright as the sun, majestic as the stars in procession?" (Song of Solomon 6:10)

The odds are that you are more attractive than you think you are. At least four areas of attractiveness draw other people to you. If you have all four in great abundance, then you are more attractive to others than those of us who have only one or two. The secret is to understand all four areas, evaluate where you are strong and where you are not so strong, and then develop a plan that will make you more attractive.

If you are not in a relationship, this chapter applies to you just as well as those currently in a relationship. Even the exercise about getting your partner to rate you will work for you if you follow the alternate instructions given with that exercise.

Biblical View of Attractiveness

We know that God loves us no matter what we look like, how smart we are, what condition our heart is in, or where we are spiritually. (Romans 5:8) As Paul Tarence, a Bible professor at Faulkner University, said, "God loves the unlovely and unlovable just as much as He does the lovely."

Therefore, *do not assume this chapter on attractiveness focuses on how to make you lovable or lovely*. It does not. However, it does focus on how being attractive in four areas leads us to be beautiful in our own eyes. The resulting confidence draws others closer to us – especially our spouses or potential spouses. *We aren't talking arrogance, but comfort with ourselves*.

The Bible speaks of attractiveness as a part of our coming to love another person romantically. Study the following verses from the Bible.

[Note that in the Song of Solomon the similes are pertinent to their time. For example, "hair like a flock of goats" may not be the best compliment to give today, but in Solomon's time it was a description of wonderful, full, luxuriant hair. The key is to understand that Solomon and his wife compliment the beauty they see in each other as they share how that beauty affects them. They are drawn to each other as they see attractiveness in each other.]

- [Solomon's wife describes herself] *I am black but lovely...(Song of Solomon 1:5)*

- [And] *I was a wall, and my breasts were like towers; then I became in his eyes as one who finds peace.* (Song of Solomon 8:10)

- [Solomon describes his wife] *How beautiful you are, my darling, how beautiful you are! Your eyes are like doves behind your veil; your hair is like a flock of goats that have descended from Mount Gilead. Your teeth are like a flock of newly shorn ewes...Your lips are like a scarlet thread, and your mouth is lovely. Your temples are like a slice of a pomegranate behind your veil. Your neck is like the tower of David...Your two breasts are like two fawns, twins of a gazelle, which feed among the lilies...You are altogether beautiful, my darling, and there is no blemish in you.* (Song of Solomon 4:1-7)

- [And] *How beautiful are your feet...The curves of your hips are like jewels, the work of the hands of an artist. Your navel is like a round goblet which never lacks mixed wine; your belly is like a heap of wheat fenced about with lilies...Your neck is like a tower of ivory, your eyes like the pools in Heshbon...your nose is like the tower of Lebanon...Your head crowns you like Carmel, and the flowing locks of your head are like purple threads; the king is captivated by your tresses. How beautiful and how delightful you are, my love, with all your charms! Your stature is like a palm tree, and your breasts are like its clusters. I said, "I will climb the palm tree, I will take hold of its fruit stalks." Oh, may your breasts be like clusters of the vine, and the fragrance of your breath like apples, and your mouth like the best wine! It goes down smoothly for my beloved, flowing gently through the lips...* (Song of Solomon 7:1-9)

- [Solomon's wife describes him.] *My beloved is dazzling and ruddy, outstanding among ten thousand. His head is like gold, pure gold; his locks are like clusters of dates, and black as a raven. His eyes are like doves, beside streams of water, bathed in milk, and reposed in their setting. His cheeks are like a bed of balsam, banks of sweet-scented herbs; his lips are lilies, dripping with liquid myrrh. His hands are rods of gold set with beryl; his abdomen is carved ivory inlaid with sapphires. His legs are pillars of alabaster set on pedestals of pure gold; his appearance is like Lebanon, choice as the cedars. His mouth is full of sweetness. And he is wholly desirable. This is my beloved and this is my friend, O daughters of Jerusalem.* (Song of Solomon 5:10-16)

As you can see from just this one book in the Bible, believing oneself attractive is important to being attractive to others. (Note the wife's descriptions of herself.) Additionally, when another finds us attractive, s/he is drawn to us in a way that may result in romantic love.

That is why we start with attractiveness as we learn the LovePath. We do so with the full assurance that God recognizes it in romantic relationships, especially marriage.

The Four Areas of Attractiveness

To make this easier to remember, we explain attractiveness by an acronym – PIES: **P**hysical, **I**ntellectual, **E**motional, and **S**piritual. If you're not religious, do not skip the last one. While spirituality definitely encompasses religion, our definition here refers to inner beliefs and values that you have, whether you are religious or not.

You may think of attractiveness in the corresponding words.

Physical = Body
Intellectual = Mind
Emotional = Heart
Spiritual = Soul

Complete these exercises, no matter how tough that might be. This chapter could be the beginning of a stronger self-confidence, self-esteem, and self-image than you have ever had. It also may lead to a deeper love as you traverse the LovePath.

Physical = Body

> Now when evening came David arose from his bed and walked around on the roof of the king's house, and from the roof he saw a woman bathing; and the woman was very beautiful in appearance. (2 Samuel 11:2) Read 2 Samuel 11 for the full story of the physical attraction between David and Bathsheba.

Take a good look at yourself and do it with complete honesty. Do not be too humble or hard on yourself and do not be too vain or generous. Consider everything. As Paul said in Romans 12:3: *"For by the grace given to me I say to everyone among you not to think of himself more highly than he ought to think, but to think with sober judgment, each according to the measure of faith that God has assigned."*

To get your view of how attractive you are now, we ask you to rate yourself on the following. Use the nine-point scale below to rate where you believe you are in physical attraction. Base your score on what you feel physical attractiveness is **as perceived by your spouse**.

If you are not in a relationship, base your rating on what you believe is important about physical attraction to potential companions.

Do not worry if your score is less than you wish - nearly everyone's is. We do not put you through this exercise to make you feel badly about yourself. We do it only as a baseline from which to start. Later we will ask you to get the opinion of another person about you. It may make you feel better than you anticipate.

Unattractive   Attractive

   1   2   3   4   5   6   7   8   9

PHYSICAL RATING FROM ANOTHER PERSON

If you have enough emotional strength to handle it, ask your spouse to honestly rate you on these same scale. You will have to give him/her permission to be completely honest. That means that you must promise – and keep that promise – that you will not react negatively in any way. This means no anger, arguments, sulking, pointing out his/her flaws, crying, or anything of the sort. If you cannot do that, do not complete this exercise with your spouse.

If you do not wish to do this with your spouse, ask a friend who will be honest with you. However, you must give him/her permission to be honest and promise that you will not react in a negative manner.

If you are not in a relationship, ask a friend that you know will tell you the truth to complete these questions about you. You must give him/her permission to be completely honest. If you react negatively to your friend, you will hurt your relationship.

Instructions to the spouse or friend doing the scoring: Make sure the person asking you to rate him/her is willing for you to be completely honest. This exercise is designed to help people grow in physical attractiveness as best they can at their ages and situations in life. It is to give them a starting place.

If you are a spouse, choose the number on the following scale based on your perceptions about physical attraction. If you are a friend, choose the number on the following scale based on the perceptions of physical attraction you believe are held by his/her spouse. If the person is not in a relationship, rate based on the perception potential companions will likely have.

Unattractive   Attractive

1   2   3   4   5   6   7   8   9

TIME TO TALK

Talk with the person who rated your attractiveness.

- **First**, have the person tell you why s/he rated you as s/he did.
- **Second**, ask the rater to tell you your physically attractive features. Feel free to ask questions and even to revel in what your rater says about your attractiveness.
- **Third**, ask the person what s/he believes you could do to become even more attractive. Talk openly and honestly, without defensiveness.

TIME TO WRITE

Note in the space below all the areas in which you are currently attractive so that you have confidence in what you already are.

HOW YOU CAN BECOME MORE PHYSICALLY ATTRACTIVE

Decide on two things that you will do to become more attractive.

Do not write anything below that you likely will not do. Put only those things that you will commit yourself to do. It might be something such as, "I'll go to a stylist and find the right hair style for me," or maybe, "I'll join the gym and get myself toned and in good shape."

To make this more powerful, put next to each the date you will start doing the thing you have written and, if appropriate, the date you set as your goal to complete it. (For example, if your action is to dress better, it will not have an end date.) If it should have a goal date, it might be something such as, "I'll join Weight Watchers ® by the first of next month, and will be at my target weight within nine months."

Write your commitments here:

1.

Start date _____ Goal date _____

2.

Start date _____ Goal date _____

If you do what you have written above, you will become more physically attractive in your own eyes. That is the most important thing. If you also become more physically attractive to your spouse, wonderful. That will help you both grow on the LovePath. However, do NOT forget that physical attractiveness is just one of the four areas of attractiveness and it is NOT important that you be physically beautiful by Madison Avenue standards to have a wonderful and fulfilling life and love. Be the best you can be at your age and situation in life. Don't compare yourself to others; just be the healthy you.

Intellectual = Mind

> Now the man's name was Nabal, and his wife's name was Abigail. And the woman was intelligent and beautiful in appearance, but the man was harsh and evil in his dealings... (1 Samuel 25:3) Read 1 Samuel 25 for the full story of the intellectual attraction between David and

Now it is time to take a good look inside you rather than at the outside. As before, do not be too humble or hard on yourself and do not be too vain or generous.

As you read in *Your LovePath*, there is an attraction called Intellectual Attraction – the attraction of another to your mind and your ability to communicate and to stimulate the other person's mind.

Score each question based on what you feel intellectual attractiveness is **as perceived by your spouse**.

If you are not in a relationship, base your rating on what you believe is important about intellectual attraction to potential companions.

Unattractive   Attractive

1   2   3   4   5   6   7   8   9

INTELLECTUAL RATING FROM ANOTHER PERSON

Ask your spouse to honestly rate you on this scale. Give permission for complete honesty.

If you do not wish to do this with your spouse, ask a friend who will be honest with you. However, you must give him/her permission to be honest and promise that you will not react in a negative manner.

If you are not in a relationship, ask a friend that you know will tell you the truth to complete these questions about you. You must give him/her permission to be completely honest. If you react negatively to your friend, you will hurt your relationship.

Instructions to the spouse or friend doing the scoring: Make sure the person asking you to rate him/her is willing for you to be completely honest. This exercise is designed to help people grow in intellectual attractiveness as best they can at their ages and situations in life. It is to give them a starting place.

If you are a spouse, choose the number on the following scale based on your perceptions about intellectual attraction. If you are a friend, choose the number on the following scale based on the perceptions of intellectual attraction you believe are held by his/her spouse. If the person is not in a relationship, rate based on the perception potential companions will likely have.

Unattractive   Attractive

1   2   3   4   5   6   7   8   9

TIME TO TALK

Talk with the person who rated your attractiveness.

- **First,** have the person tell you why s/he rated you as s/he did.
- **Second,** ask the rater to tell you your intellectually attractive features. Feel free to ask questions and even to revel in what your rater says about your attractiveness.
- **Third,** ask the person what s/he believes you could do to become even more intellectually attractive. Talk openly and honestly, without defensiveness.

TIME TO WRITE

Note in the space below all the areas in which you are currently attractive so that you have confidence in what you already are.

HOW YOU CAN BECOME MORE INTELLECTUALLY ATTRACTIVE

Decide on two things you will do to become more attractive.

It might be something such as, "I'll sign up for night classes, or one offered on the Internet," or maybe, "I'll get a book on communication and read it;" perhaps, "I'll join a book club to stimulate my thinking and broaden my mind."

Put next to each the date you will start doing the thing you have written and, if appropriate, the date you set as your goal to complete it.

Write your commitments here:

1.

Start date _____ Goal date _____

2.

Start date _____ Goal date _____

Emotional = Heart

Isaac brought her into the tent of his mother Sarah, and he married Rebekah. So she became his wife, and he loved her; and Isaac was comforted after his mother's death. (Genesis 24:67)

Read Genesis 24 for the full story of the emotional attraction between Isaac and Rebekah.

The editorial review of the book *Emotional Intelligence* by Daniel Goleman on www.Amazon.com says, "He defines emotional intelligence in terms of self-awareness, altruism, personal motivation, empathy, and the ability to love and be loved by friends, partners, and family members."

In short, it has two areas of importance:

- understanding yourself, your feelings, your goals, your behaviors, and the like

- understanding others, especially their feelings

Use the nine-point scale below to rate where you believe you are in emotional attractiveness. Rate yourself based on what you feel emotional attractiveness is **as perceived by your spouse**.

If you are not in a relationship, base your rating on what you believe is important about emotional attraction to potential companions.

Unattractive   Attractive

| 1 | 2 | 3 | 4 | 5 | 6 | 7 | 8 | 9 |

EMOTIONAL RATING FROM ANOTHER PERSON

Ask your spouse to honestly rate you on these same questions.

If you do not wish to do this with your spouse, ask a friend who will be honest with you. However, you must give him/her permission to be honest and promise that you will not react in a negative manner.

If you are not in a relationship, ask a friend that you know will tell you the truth to complete these questions about you. You must give him/her permission to be completely honest. If you react negatively to your friend, you will hurt your relationship.

Instructions to the spouse or friend doing the scoring: Make sure the person asking you to rate him/her is willing for you to be completely honest. This exercise is designed to help people grow in emotional attractiveness as best they can at their ages and situations in life. It is to give them a starting place.

If you are a spouse, choose the number on the following scale based on your perceptions about emotional attraction. If you are a friend, choose the number on the following scale based on the perceptions of emotional attraction you believe are held by his/her spouse. If the person is not in a relationship, rate based on the perception potential companions will likely have.

Unattractive   Attractive

1   2   3   4   5   6   7   8   9

TIME TO TALK

Talk with the person who rated your attractiveness.

First, have the person tell you why s/he rated you as s/he did.

Second, ask the rater to tell you your emotionally attractive features. Feel free to ask questions and even to revel in what your rater says about your attractiveness.

Third, ask the person what s/he believes you could do to become even more attractive. Talk openly and honestly, without defensiveness.

TIME TO WRITE

Note in the space below all the areas in which you are currently attractive so that you have confidence in what you already are.

HOW YOU CAN BECOME MORE EMOTIONALLY ATTRACTIVE

Decide on two things that you will do to become more attractive. It might be something such as, "I'll ask a few trusted friends to help me become more emotionally vulnerable," or maybe, "I'll ask my spouse how s/he would like for me to demonstrate love."

Put next to each the date you will start doing the thing you have written and, if appropriate, the date you set as your goal to complete it.

Write your commitments here:

1.

Start date _____ Goal date _____

2.

Start date _____ Goal date _____

Spiritual = Soul

> At this, she bowed down with her face to the ground. She exclaimed, "Why have I found such favor in your eyes that you notice me—a foreigner?"
>
> Boaz replied, "I've been told all about what you have done for your mother-in-law since the death of your husband—how you left your father and mother and your homeland and came to live with a people you did not know before. May the LORD repay you for what you have done. May you be richly rewarded by the LORD, the God of Israel, under whose wings you have come to take refuge." (Ruth 2:10-12)

Beliefs and values begin when you are a child influenced by parents or caregivers. Later your teachers and friends may modify them. If you have religious experience, it expands them.

Spirituality in the context of attractiveness has to do with a person's **beliefs and values** that draw another person closer. As with all other areas of attraction, it is not something that occurs just at the beginning of a relationship, but a dimension that continues throughout.

In most cases, the words "beliefs" and "values" are used interchangeably. If one were to try to differentiate between the two: Beliefs are how we think things are and what we think is true; values are what we think people ought to do. Think of beliefs as the truths you embrace. Those beliefs lead to what you value as important conduct in life – the standards you embrace about how you and others should act.

Use the nine-point scale below to rate where you believe you are in spiritual attractiveness. Rate yourself based on what you feel spiritual attractiveness is **as perceived by your spouse**.

If you are not in a relationship, base your rating on what you believe is important about spiritual attraction to potential companions.

Unattractive   Attractive

1   2   3   4   5   6   7   8   9

SPIRITUAL RATING FROM ANOTHER PERSON

Ask your spouse to honestly rate you on these same questions.

If you do not wish to do this with your spouse, ask a friend who will be honest with you. However, you must give him/her permission to be honest and promise that you will not react in a negative manner.

If you are not in a relationship, ask a friend that you know will tell you the truth to complete these questions about you. You must give him/her permission to be completely honest. If you react negatively to your friend, you will hurt your relationship.

Instructions to the spouse or friend doing the scoring: Make sure the person asking you to rate him/her is willing for you to be completely honest. This exercise is designed to help people grow in spiritual attractiveness as best they can at their ages and situations in life. It is to give them a starting place.

If you are a spouse, choose the number on the following scale based on your perceptions about spiritual attraction. If you are a friend, choose the number on the following scale based on the perceptions of spiritual attraction you believe are held by his/her spouse. If the person is not in a relationship, rate based on the perception potential companions will likely have.

Unattractive   Attractive

1   2   3   4   5   6   7   8   9

TIME TO TALK

Talk with the person who rated your attractiveness.

First, have the person tell you why s/he rated you as s/he did.

Second, ask the rater to tell you your spiritually attractive features. Feel free to ask questions and even to revel in what your rater says about your attractiveness.

Third, ask the person what s/he believes you could do to become even more attractive. Talk openly and honestly, without defensiveness.

TIME TO WRITE

Note in the space below all the areas in which you are currently attractive so that you have confidence in what you already are.

HOW YOU CAN BECOME MORE SPIRITUALLY ATTRACTIVE

Decide on two things that you will do to become more attractive.

It might be something such as, "I'll sit down with a spiritual person I trust and evaluate my beliefs and values," or maybe, "I'll ask my spouse how we can bring our beliefs and values into greater harmony."

Put next to each the date you will start doing the thing you have written and, if appropriate, the date you set as your goal to complete it.

Write your commitments here:

1.

Start date _____ Goal date _____

2.

Start date _____ Goal date _____

If You Are Not In a Relationship

As you evaluate individuals with whom you may be interested in developing a relationship, the scales above could be valuable. Rate him/her on these scales. That will provide you a way to see beyond just emotions and focus on what will be important to you as you traverse the LovePath.

In Conclusion

Never forget the primary goal of increasing attractiveness is your own self-esteem, self-confidence, and self-image. You do not have to become more attractive to be loved. True love, as we will see in the next chapter, occurs when another person accepts you as you truly are, not because of some specific characteristic.

Even as we write that, we acknowledge what nearly every unattached person in America knows: the more attractive you are, the more people want to move closer to you. That is not just physically attractive, but also intellectually, emotionally, and spiritually attractive. Ever seen a gorgeous woman with a guy who is not her equal on the physical attractiveness scale? Maybe a hunk with a woman who seems not to match? That is because they were attracted strongly by the other areas more than they were simply by the physical. Therefore, do not worry if you are not a hunk or a beauty queen. The greatest beauty that one displays is that which comes from the belief that he or she is attractive. Do the things you have committed to do for yourself in the pages of this chapter. It will give you confidence that will draw others to you.

If you are in a relationship, becoming more attractive should not be a requirement to continue the relationship. As we have said all along, we all want to be loved for our true selves, not some picture we paint. However, relationships grow and prosper when each spouse purposely continues to grow in attractiveness within the parameters of his/her age and situation in life. It demonstrates to the other that you care, that you want to give all you can give, and that you will not let yourself deteriorate by neglecting body, mind, heart, or soul.

That is thinking of the other – selflessness – while taking care of you. What a wonderful combination. Do it as long as you both shall live.

As you write your answers on the next page, do so alone. Later, when you have a quiet time with no interruptions – for example,

- phones off

- kids in bed

- TV banished

Talk with your husband, wife, fiancé, boyfriend, girlfriend, or a dear friend about your answers.

Share with each other.

Please, no judgments, defensiveness, or disagreements. Just listen as best you can to each other so that you may understand how the other person feels. *This is not a time to debate or correct.*

It is a time to listen and learn. To understand. To empathize/ Do that and you will grow.

Daily Thoughts and Prayers

Day One

Spend a few minutes meditating and talking with God about positives about your physical attractiveness. Jot your thoughts here.

The one thing that I will make sure I pray about today that will help me appreciate the way God made me is….

Day Two

Spend a few minutes meditating and talking with God about positives about your intellectual attractiveness. Jot your thoughts here.

The one thing that I will make sure I pray about today that will help me appreciate the way God made me is….

Day Three

Spend a few minutes meditating and talking with God about positives about your emotional attractiveness. Jot your thoughts here.

The one thing that I will make sure I pray about today that will help me appreciate the way God made me is....

DAY FOUR

Spend a few minutes meditating and talking with God about positives about your spiritual attractiveness. Jot your thoughts here.

The one thing that I will make sure I pray about today that will help me appreciate the way God made me is....

DAY FIVE

Meditate today about why you are loveable—not arrogantly or in vain—but in true evaluation of self... Jot your thoughts here.

The one thing that I will make sure I pray about today that will help me appreciate the way God made me is....

Class Sharing Time

In your next group meeting, you will spend a few minutes sharing with your group. Before coming to class, think these through and write your answers. What we think and write about has dramatically more effect on us than what we talk about. Write your answers so that you get the most from this study.

- In which of the four areas of attraction did you friend / spouse / etc. rate you the highest? What did they say about you that either surprised you or affirmed you in a good way?

- Who has been most influential in affecting the way you view yourself in the area of physical attractiveness? How did that person (or those people) affect the way you view yourself?

- Use the same process as in the question above to explain who influenced you in your view of your intellectual, emotional, and spiritual attraction.

- What event(s) in your life most affected the way you view your attractiveness in each of the PIES?

- How do you think God views your physical, intellectual, emotional, and spiritual attractiveness?

Notes as you watch the DVD

Chapter 3 – Acceptance

Understanding the key to love...

Do nothing from selfishness or empty conceit, but with humility of mind regard one another as more important than yourselves; (Philippians 2:3)

Experience with thousands of couples taught us the most important thing in a relationship is respect. That means giving esteem and honor, as well as demonstrating regard and consideration to each other. Most of the couples we see in our workshop for marriages in crisis, *LovePath 911*, offer little or no respect to each other (or at least one to the other). Healthy, happy couples do.

Respect has to do with acceptance. As you read in *Your LovePath*, people tend to paint a picture they believe others wish to see. We paint those pictures because we want others to accept us. However, what we really want – deep in our hearts – is to be loved for the person we are rather than the picture we paint.

To have the deepest love possible with your spouse, you must learn to accept yourself as you are and your companion as s/he is.

If you are not in a relationship, this chapter applies to you just as well as those married. Acceptance is the most important LovePath step for falling in love.

Biblical View of Acceptance

As noted in chapter two, we do not have to meet any standard for God to love us as we are. We do not have to paint a picture that we hope He will love. He sees into our hearts, knowing who we are, and loves us for ourselves. For emphasis, we underline certain phrases in some of the following passages.

"...God sees not as man sees, for man looks at the outward appearance, but the LORD looks at the heart." (1 Samuel 16:7)

Ephesians 2 speaks of our sinfulness thoroughly known to God. Immediately after describing human transgressions, Paul writes that God loves us anyway: *"But God, being rich in mercy, because of His great love with which He loved us, even when we were dead in our transgressions, made us alive together with Christ (by grace you have been saved),"* (Ephesians 2:4-5)

God tells us that we are all sinners (Romans 3:10) who *"fall short of the glory of God."* (Romans 3:23) Yet, *"...while we were still helpless, at the right time Christ died for the ungodly. For one will hardly die for a righteous* *man; though perhaps for the good man someone would dare even to die. But <u>God demonstrates His own love toward us, in that while we were yet sinners,</u> Christ died for us."* (Romans 5:6-8)

In the New Testament you will find that Jesus treated sinners with great respect, though He did not accept their sinful actions. The story of the sinful woman in Luke 7:36-50 demonstrates the tremendous love Jesus felt for a woman that an entire town rejected. He knew her sins and loved her anyway – just as she was. That wonderful love (acceptance) from Jesus led her, as it did many, from wicked ways to the way of light. He loves us as we are, before we change to be what He wishes us to be.

It was the hypocrites that Jesus treated with harshness. The entire 23rd chapter of Matthew consists of Jesus condemning – rejecting – those who pretended to be righteous but were not. When we acknowledge our weaknesses, failings, and transgressions, without trying to paint a picture that we are someone other than our real selves, God showers us with love and acceptance. If we try to paint a picture for Him to love – thinking that we hide our real selves – He rejects us.

In His teaching about love and acceptance, Jesus reiterated an Old Testament principle as a New Testament truth: *"You shall love the Lord your God with all your heart, and with all your soul, and with all your mind. This is the great and foremost commandment. The second is like it, 'You shall love your neighbor as yourself. On these two commandments depend the whole Law and the Prophets."* (Matthew 22:37-40) Life shows the truth of that passage, particularly in that those who cannot love themselves do not love others. It is in acceptance of self that we find the direction to light and life.

Let us explain that in modern terms.

What is Acceptance?

If you comprehend the following, you will understand the foundation of true love.

"The most crucial dimension for falling in love is acceptance. I will not love a person that I do not accept, even if that person is me."

Acceptance does not always mean agreement. One definition of acceptance is "tolerance without resentment." In the way we use the term, it means accepting that something exists or is true whether you want it to be or not. For example, a husband may not agree with his wife's political views, but he can accept that they are valid (true) to her, and, therefore, should be respected. He does not harangue her to agree with his views, does not treat her as if she is unknowledgeable, nor behave as if he is superior because he feels his political views are correct and hers are not. In short, giving acceptance to another person is to show respect to that person as your equal, especially when you do not agree with or like what that person believes, thinks, or feels.

Each of us wants to be validated for who we are, what we think, and what we feel. Receiving understanding and respect provides us validation.

Loving Self

The most important thing in love is acceptance. People who interact with love and affection with others must first love themselves in the right way. Not too much. Not too little. But we are all people with value and worth – consider Psalm 139:13-14: *"For you formed my inward parts; you knitted me together in my mother's womb. I praise you, for I am fearfully and wonderfully made. Wonderful are your works; my soul knows it very well."*

Sometimes we have trouble accepting ourselves as we are because of events that occurred earlier in our lives.

LIFE EXPERIENCES THAT WERE CREATED BY YOUR ACTIONS

Think of anything you have done in your life that negatively affects your acceptance of yourself. Write a brief description of it here, just enough to evoke your memory.

LIFE EXPERIENCES THAT WERE CREATED BY THE ACTIONS OF OTHERS

Think of anything done to you by others that negatively affects your acceptance of yourself. Write just enough to evoke the memory.

LIFE EXPERIENCES THAT NO ONE CAUSED

Think of anything life has thrown at you, not caused by any person, that negatively affects your acceptance of yourself. Write a brief description of it here.

Look through the things you have written in the three areas above. To change their negative effect on how you accept yourself, there are four possible solutions.

WHAT CAN YOU DO TO OVERCOME NEGATIVES CAUSED BY YOU?

Sometimes facing a wrong we have done is the best way to overcome it. That may mean confessing. It might mean apologizing. In some cases, it could be returning something to someone else. You have to decide what action, if any, would bring you inner peace and acceptance.

Therefore confess your sins to each other and pray for each other so that you may be healed. The prayer of a righteous man is powerful and effective. (James 5:16)

Note: Do not do anything that may harm others - for example, confessing to your best friend, "I slept with your husband."

Write here any actions that you can do to overcome any of the negatives you listed above.

WHAT IMPERFECTIONS OR FLAWS SHOULD YOU ACCEPT ABOUT YOURSELF?

The secret to acceptance is to accept the imperfections and flaws that you have. We call it satisfied dissatisfaction. The famous psychologist Carl Rogers said, "The curious paradox is that when I accept myself as I am, then I change…we cannot change, we cannot move away from what we are, until we thoroughly accept what we are. Then change seems to come almost unnoticed"

Write here those things you need to accept about yourself, even if you want to change.

WHOM DO YOU NEED TO FORGIVE?

You will learn a great deal more about forgiveness in chapter eight. Right now, think of it this way: Hating, wanting vengeance, and hanging on to hurts seldom affects the person who hurt you. Instead, it becomes a ball and chain that ties you to that person in your mind and heart. Forgiving does not absolve the other person from guilt or responsibility; it sets you free from the pain of the hurt.

Forgiveness means: 1) deciding the other person is flawed and is not the Devil; 2) deciding to give up any right you have to vengeance. If you wish, it may also mean, 3) reconciling with the person who hurt you. However, that step is not required for you to find inner peace. Forgiveness allows you to accept that what that person did to you happened and you cannot go back in history and make it not happen. Decide that you will not let it affect the rest of your life.

Let all bitterness and wrath and anger and clamor and slander be put away from you, along with all malice. Be kind to one another, tender-hearted, forgiving each other, just as God in Christ also has forgiven you. (Ephesians 4:31-32)

What do you need to forgive someone for? Write that here.

WHAT NEGATIVE EXPERIENCES FROM LIFE DO YOU NEED TO ACCEPT?

Acceptance in life means accepting that history cannot be changed. For example, the final stage of grief when a person loses a loved one is to finally accept that s/he is gone and never coming back. That acceptance brings inner peace. What do you need to accept as history that cannot be changed?

If You Are Not In a Relationship

Make sure that you have done the exercises in the section of this chapter about self.

DEAL BREAKERS

It is time to think about what you will not accept in another person who may be a potential partner. We refer to them as "deal breakers." Use them to evaluate any person with whom you might develop a relationship. Remember, it is easier to end an unhealthy relationship early on than it is later.

Think of personality traits, behaviors, life conditions, religious practices, previous experience, morality, or anything else you will not accept -- deal breakers -- in developing a relationship with another. Write them here and check them regularly as you consider potential companions.

In Conclusion

If you feel accepted as you are, you feel loved. If you feel accepted only if you paint a picture that you believe the other person wants you to be, you will doubt the depth of his/her love.

When you accept another as s/he is, that person feels loved. If s/he feels accepted by you only when they paint the picture that you expect, s/he will doubt the depth of your love.

Learn to accept yourself as you are so that you can learn to accept the one you love as s/he is. This is the most important dimension of love. There is great research indicating that couples work through even the most difficult of problems when they learn to accept each other as they are; tolerance without resentment.

Love works better when you live with satisfied dissatisfaction. That means accepting yourself and your beloved as you each are while always wanting to grow.

Moving On

After the next section **Daily Thoughts and Prayers** are questions that you need to answer before coming to the next class session. Please make sure you write your answers to those before coming to class.

Daily Thoughts and Prayers

Day One

Spend a few minutes meditating and talking with God about how He accepts you as you are. Jot your thoughts here.

The one thing that I will make sure I pray about today that will help me learn to accept others as God accepts me is....

Day Two

Spend a few minutes meditating and talking with God about how you can accept others similar to the way He does. Jot your thoughts here.

The one thing that I will make sure I pray about today that will help me learn to accept others as God accepts me is....

Day Three

Spend a few minutes meditating and talking with God about what it means for you to accept yourself as you are, instead of feeling that you have to be or do more to be acceptable. Jot your thoughts here.

The one thing that I will make sure I pray about today that will help me learn to accept others as God accepts me is....

Day Four

Spend a few minutes meditating and talking with God about what it means for you to accept Him as He is, instead of what you might want Him to be. Jot your thoughts here.

The one thing that I will make sure I pray about today that will help me learn to accept others as God accepts me is....

Day Five

Spend a few minutes meditating and talking with God about how you have changed for the better because He loves you as you are, an imperfect human. Jot your thoughts here.

The one thing that I will make sure I pray about today that will help me learn to accept others as God accepts me is....

Class Sharing Time

Before coming to class, think these through and write your answers.

- Using the following scale, circle the statement that best reflects how you honestly feel about the following sentence. "I accept, respect, and love myself as I am."

    1. *Strongly Disagree*

    2. *Moderately Disagree*

    3. *Mildly Disagree*

    4. *Not sure.*

    5. *Mildly Agree*

    6. *Moderately Agree*

    7. *Strongly Agree*

- Why did you give yourself that rating? Please be as specific as possible.

- What has been the most difficult thing for you to forgive another person for? How did you do it (or how will you do it?)

- Why is forgiving a crucial aspect of loving?

- This workbook states that you cannot love anyone that you do not accept as they are, even if that person is you. Do you agree or disagree? Please explain.

Notes as you watch the DVD

Chapter 4 – Why We Fall Madly In Love

Storm warning along the path…

In the course of time, Amnon son of David fell in love with Tamar, the beautiful sister of Absalom son of David. Amnon became frustrated to the point of illness on account of his sister Tamar, for she was a virgin, and it seemed impossible for him to do anything to her. Now Amnon had a friend named Jonadab son of Shimeah, David's brother. Jonadab was a very shrewd man. He asked Amnon, "Why do you, the king's son, look so haggard morning after morning? Won't you tell me?" Amnon said to him, "I'm in love with Tamar, my brother Absalom's sister." (2 Samuel 13:1-4)

L imerence is that intense romantic state in which you constantly think of the one you love, worry that s/he might abandon you, and long to be with him/her. Sometimes researchers refer to it as being "madly in love." Your world revolves around the person researchers refer to as the "limerence object," usually abbreviated to L.O.

It is important that you read chapter four in *Your LovePath* before you do the exercises in this chapter. That chapter provides information about limerence so that you may more fully understand it. We do not repeat that information in this workbook.

Biblical View of Limerence

The Bible does not use the word limerence; however, the concept is as old as humankind. Limerence – as you shall see in this chapter – could be described as romantic love on steroids. Sometimes it is holy, such as when spouses feel this intense emotion for each other. Sometimes it is unholy, particularly when it leads a person – married or single – to violate the laws of God.

We discuss limerence in detail in chapter four of *Your LovePath*. You would do well to stop here until you read that chapter so that the scriptures and principles we share carry value for you. In short, the understanding of limerence given in the book provides a better understanding of certain scriptures.

For example, romantic love can be wonderful and lead to long-lived relationships. As we saw earlier in the Song of Solomon, the love Solomon and his wife had for each other was passionate and intense. However, as we see from the arranged marriages in the Old Testament, limerence is not a requirement for developing a fulfilling, life-long love.

The thing to remember is that the intense emotions known as limerence may lead one to make decisions and commit actions that negatively affect the remainder of his/her life. As Proverbs 5:3-20 warns,

For the lips of an adulteress drip honey, and smoother than oil is her speech; but in the end she is bitter as wormwood, sharp as a two-edged sword. Her feet go down to death, her steps lay hold of Sheol. She does not ponder the path of life; her ways are unstable, she does not know it.

Now then, my sons, listen to me, and do not depart from the words of my mouth. Keep your way far from her, and do not go near the door of her house, lest you give your vigor to others, and your years to the cruel one; lest strangers be filled with your strength, and your hard-earned goods go to the house of an alien; and you groan at your latter end, when your flesh and your body are consumed; and you say, "How I have hated instruction! And my heart spurned reproof! And I have not listened to the voice of my teachers, nor inclined my ear to my instructors! I was almost in utter ruin in the midst of the assembly and congregation."

Drink water from your own cistern, and fresh water from your own well. Should your springs be dispersed abroad, streams of water in the streets? Let them be yours alone, and not for strangers with you. Let your fountain be blessed, and rejoice in the wife of your youth. As a loving hind and a graceful doe, let her breasts satisfy you at all times; be exhilarated always with her love. For why should you, my son, be exhilarated with an adulteress, and embrace the bosom of a foreigner?

Anyone drawn into an intense emotional relationship that is not holy should carefully consider the passage above. It applies equally to women as to men. Notice the key points made:

- It begins sweet as honey, but ends in bitterness and sorrow.

- A person in this situation is unstable, not considering the longer path of life, and is not aware of their instability.

- When one gives up a holy relationship for one that is unholy (violating the will of God):

  o Future life becomes cruel – compliments of the evil one – because you sacrificed real life (vigor) for the person you thought you loved more.

  o Someone else will take the life you had, because you abandoned it. (Your possessions, your family – if your mate moves on – and all the things that gave your life strength.)

- Too late one comes to realization that s/he should have listened to those who warned of the consequences of this path.

- Rather than seeking intense emotional love, satisfy yourself with the companionship of your spouse.

o Passion may dwindle as you grow older, but your spouse is the one with whom you must share life, even when the fires are not as intense as they once were.

o Real satisfaction comes through a relationship with one who loves you for a lifetime, not the one who loves you until passion fades.

For those who are not married and experiencing limerence, we remind you not to let limerence lead you into a sexual relationship before you marry. Let marriage be held in honor among all, and let the marriage bed be undefiled; for fornicators and adulterers God will judge. (Hebrews 13:4)

WHEN LIMERENCE IS OKAY AND WHEN IT IS NOT

Limerence does not occur for everyone. Many couples meet, fall in love, marry, and live their entire lives together without ever having had the experience. You do not have to experience limerence to develop a deep and lasting love. As your read in *Your LovePath*, limerence is temporary, lasting anywhere from six months to three years. Then it goes away and does not occur again in your relationship with your L.O.

When two people are free to love each other without violating their beliefs and values, and without harming or destroying an existing committed relationship, limerence is great. However, when it violates the beliefs and values of either, or negatively affects a committed relationship, it brings pain and misery.

We ask those leaving spouses because they are in limerence with another, "Do you really want to make a life-altering decision based on an emotion that will last three years at best? Are you prepared for the major letdown that will occur when limerence ends and you look back at all you gave up to be with your lover?"

We have seen so many who three years or less into the limerent relationship regret following their intense emotions, ignoring life as it really is and really will be.

A Checkup for Yourself

Some people are so enthralled by the emotional high (in actuality, a chemical high) of limerence that they cannot stay in any relationship for an extended time. It appears they are just as much addicted to the thrill of limerence as are addicts pursuing other drugs. Let us see if you might be one.

1. How many times have you been in love?

2. Have any of these relationships been with a person who was in a committed relationship with another?

3. Have any of these relationships occurred with another while you were in a committed relationship (such as long-term attachment, engagement, marriage)?

4. In these relationships, do you find yourself enchanted with the emotional thrill of being so deeply in love?

What do your answers to the question above tell you about yourself? Be honest - are you going from one limerent relationship to another, sometimes leaving relationships because you no longer had the feelings you once had?

A Checkup for Your Relationship

Below is a tool that will provide you awareness if you are falling into limerence with someone other than your spouse.

The "particular person" in these questions is someone other than your spouse.

1. Is there a particular person that you feel defensive about your relationship with when other people question it?

2. Is there a particular person that you sometimes feel you share too many of your thoughts and feelings with, and that you should cut back in doing so?

3. Is there a particular person that you feel guilty about the time you spend with them, or the things you talk about?

4. Is there a particular person that is your "elevator" – the person you want to talk to or be with when you are emotionally up or emotionally down?

If you answered yes to two of the above questions, you likely will develop limerence *with* this person (if s/he reciprocates) or *for* this person (if s/he does not reciprocate.) Either way, you are going to damage your current relationship.

If You Are Not in a Relationship

Be sure that you have done the exercises in the "Checkup for Yourself" section. That is critical to understanding the way you approach relationships. If you are not a "limerence addict" as explained in that section, there are still things you need to be aware of as you evaluate potential companions.

*   If you develop limerence for a particular person, s/he may not develop limerence for you. That will hurt, but it is not the end of the world. You will get over it when one of two things happens: 1) you finally emotionally accept that there will be no reciprocation, or 2) you develop limerence for another.

*   If you move quickly from limerence with one person to limerence with another, do not trust your judgment. Ask trusted friends to help you evaluate the person and the relationship. Do not rush into a committed relationship until you are at least one year past the previous relationship.

*   It may occur that someone develops limerence for you that you do not want to be involved with. If that occurs, starve his/her limerence by clearly demonstrating that there is absolutely no reciprocation.

*   If limerence begins to develop between you and a person in a committed relationship, get away from it as quickly as you can. Do not believe the lie, "Our relationship was over long ago. I'm just waiting for _____ before divorcing/leaving." Thousands can testify to how badly that turns out.

*   If limerence develops between you and a person that is a good relationship (see the second paragraph under "When Limerence is Okay and When It is Not"), enjoy it but be careful in

making any life decisions while in that state without sound counsel. We recommend premarital counseling from a minister or counselor.

With those considerations in mind, here is a checklist you may use to evaluate your relationship when you develop limerence with another.

1. Am I really in love with this person or am I actually more in love with this feeling?

2. What are the things about this person that I find attractive other than the fact that I feel so much for him/her?

3. Am I honestly evaluating what a future with this person would be like, or am I allowing myself to think with a "fairy tale" mindset?

4. Do I honestly believe that I would wake up with this person when I'm seventy years old and be thankful that s/he is there?

5. How do the friends and relatives I trust to be objective evaluate this person?

6. Would I want my children to be like this person in every way that is important to me?

7. Who could be hurt – including me – if this relationship develops to long-term commitment?

8. Would a long-term relationship with this person help me grow, or would it likely keep me stagnant or even deteriorate?

9. Can I truly trust this person with my heart, my life, my money, my children, or anyone or anything else valuable to me?

10. Because I feel such intense emotion, am I overlooking this person's flaws that could harm or destroy our relationship in the future?

In Conclusion

Limerence is something that may or may not happen as you traverse the LovePath.

Never trust your judgment while in limerence. Get wise counsel from others that you trust, as recommended in Proverbs 19:20: *"Listen to advice and accept instruction, and in the end you will be wise."* If it does occur for you, do everything you can to not let it overcome your knowledge, wisdom, and instincts.

Do not let limerence occur between you and another who is in a committed relationship. It will lead only to heartbreak. Do not let limerence develop with another if you are in a committed relationship. Live up to your commitments. Be a person of integrity and character.

Accept the fact that limerence is short-lived. If you experience it, it will last anywhere from six months to three years. When it fades, do not think that the relationship is no longer a good or viable one. Read the chapter in Your LovePath so that you may see the real glue of life is not limerence, but the bonding that comes after limerence.

If you bonded without experiencing limerence, do not feel cheated. Actually, you may be the one who did it the better way and will have a better relationship as long as you live.

Daily Thoughts and Prayers

Day One

Spend a few minutes meditating and talking with God about why He made us in a way that we can feel deep joy and ecstasy in love relationships. Jot your thoughts here.

The one thing that I will make sure I pray about today that will help me love wisely is....

Day Two

Spend a few minutes meditating and talking with God about any love experiences you have had that didn't turn out as you expected them to. Jot your thoughts here.

The one thing that I will make sure I pray about today that will help me love wisely is....

Day Three

Spend a few minutes meditating and talking with God about why He didn't intend for romantic love to always be ecstasy and bliss. Jot your thoughts here.

The one thing that I will make sure I pray about today that will help me love wisely is....

Day Four

Spend a few minutes meditating and talking with God about what you truly and deeply want in your love relationship with your mate or future mate. Jot your thoughts here.

The one thing that I will make sure I pray about today that will help me love wisely is....

....

Day Five

Spend a few minutes meditating and talking with God about how you can experience deep feelings of love and closeness with Him. Jot your thoughts here.

The one thing that I will make sure I pray about today that will help me love wisely is....

Class Sharing Time

In your next group meeting, you will spend a few minutes sharing with your group. Before coming to class, think these through and write your answers. What we think and write about has dramatically more effect on us than what we talk about. Write your answers so that you get the most from this study.

1. Why would God make humans in such a way that they experience limerence?

2. Have you ever been hurt by a limerent relationship? (It could be your own, your spouse's, your parents', etc.) What were some of the feelings you felt?

3. What advice would you give to someone in limerence with a person they do not have a right to?

4. How could a person overcome limerence and give up a relationship that is not right? What would have to happen? Have you ever seen it happen?

5. What are ways you can safeguard your marriage (or future marriage, if you are single) to keep you or your spouse from falling into limerence with another?

Notes as you watch the DVD

Chapter 5 – Attachment

Understanding the key to relationship...

Therefore shall a man leave his father and his mother, and shall cleave unto his wife: and they shall be one flesh. (Genesis 2:24)

In chapter three we said that acceptance is the key to love. Now we wish to make a point that is just as important on the LovePath - **Attachment is the key to relationship.** The concept of "leave, cleave, and weave" – leaving your parents, cleaving to your spouse, and weaving a life with them – has been an integral part of relationships since Adam and Eve.

What makes a relationship work when the other dimensions of love fluctuate? Attachment. As you read in chapter five of *Your LovePath*, the "C" word that accompanies attachment is **commitment**. Commitment means not just being with the person you are committed to, but that you will also be there for him or her.

If You Are In a Relationship

Rate your commitment to your spouse on this nine-point scale.

Not at all				Moderately				Extremely
1	2	3	4	5	6	7	8	9

What does your score tell you about your commitment to this relationship? If you are not sure, ask your partner to rate your commitment on this scale. Then talk about the ratings each of you gave yourselves and each other.

Biblical View of Attachment

One of the most entrancing stories of commitment in the Bible is that of Jacob and Rachel in Genesis 29.

Now Laban had two daughters; the name of the older was Leah, and the name of the younger was Rachel. And Leah's eyes were weak, but Rachel was beautiful of form and face. Now Jacob loved Rachel, so he said, "I will serve you seven years for your younger daughter Rachel."...So Jacob served seven years for

Rachel and they seemed to him but a few days because of his love for her. Then Jacob said to Laban, "Give me my wife, for my time is completed"...in the evening that he [Laban] took his daughter Leah, and brought her to him [Jacob]...So it came about in the morning that, behold, it was Leah! And he said to Laban, "What is this you have done to me? Was it not for Rachel that I served with you? Why then have you deceived me?" But Laban said, "It is not the practice in our place, to marry off the younger before the first-born. "Complete the week of this one, and we will give you the other also for the service which you shall serve with me for another seven years." And Jacob did so and completed her week, and he gave him his daughter Rachel as his wife...indeed he loved Rachel more than Leah, and he served with Laban for another seven years.

This story provides an example of the attachment step of the LovePath. Not only did Jacob demonstrate commitment to his beloved Rachel, but also to his father-in-law, Laban, and his first wife, Leah.

- He offered seven years of service in exchange for taking Rachel as his wife. Faithful to his word, he served every day of those seven years.

- Though deceived into taking Leah as his wife, Jacob kept his commitments as her husband. Loving Rachel more, he nevertheless fulfilled his role as Leah's husband, giving her Reuben, Simeon, Levi, and Judah. Her sons would become heads of four of the twelve tribes of Israel.

- His commitment to marrying Rachel made his tasks a joy rather than a burden. The seven years he worked for her hand "seemed to him but a few days because of his love for her." When he discovered he must serve additional years to have her hand in marriage, he "served with Laban for another seven years."

Why would Jacob stay focused on his commitment, even to a woman he did not love (Leah)? It is because of this Biblical principle taught by Jesus Himself in Matthew 5:33-37:

You have heard that the ancients were told, "You shall not make false vows, but shall fulfill your vows to the Lord." But I say to you, make no oath at all, either by heaven, for it is the throne of God, or by the earth, for it is the footstool of His feet, or by Jerusalem, for it is the city of the great King. Nor shall you make an oath by your head, for you cannot make one hair white or black. But let your statement be, "Yes, yes" or "No, no"; and anything beyond these is of evil.

How would you sum the teaching of those verses? It means that you should do what you say. Your "yes" means "yes" and your "no" means "no." No hedging by claiming that you did not swear by something valuable or holy. If you say it, you commit to it. God expects that.

Another passage teaches the same point in Psalm 15:1-5. The New International Version makes it clearest:

LORD, who may dwell in your sanctuary? Who may live on your holy hill? He whose walk is blameless and who does what is righteous, who speaks the truth from his heart...who keeps his oath even when it hurts...He who does these things will never be shaken.

Those who live righteously, who wish to live in God's sanctuary and on His holy hill, keep their word even when it hurts. That is the commitment of the attachment step. It is the bedrock of relationship.

If You Are Not In a Relationship

To help you consider some of the reasons people choose not to commit to a relationship with a particular person, we list some of the more commonly stated reasons, along with our comments on each of those reasons.

- I may be in love with the picture but find that I do not love the person that is later revealed.

Then make sure you know whom the person really is. Read chapter four in LovePath book.

- I fear the person may love their picture of what I am instead of the person that I really am.

Is it time for you to share your secrets? See chapter four in LovePath book.

- What if I commit and then later find my true soul mate?

What if you do not? You will miss a lifetime of love waiting for a fairy tale. Besides, there are no perfect soul mates.

- I'm afraid the person will abandon me (including death).

We all take that risk. Does it hurt if they leave? Yes. If you truly cannot trust the other person with your heart because of whom or what s/he is, stop the relationship now. If you cannot trust the other person with your heart because of whom or what you are, it is time to change. Ask yourself; is this person worth the risk?

- I'm afraid that I may abandon the other person at some later date.

If you can keep your word, even on the days you do not want to, then your own integrity will not allow this to happen.

- I'm afraid I will fail.

You can but you do not have to. There are many wonderful tools available to help you be successful in a relationship.

- I fear the changes I would have to make.

Would you rather make a few changes or be alone for the rest of your life?

- I'm afraid of what the future holds.

That is why wise people live one day at a time.

- I'm afraid of replicating a bad situation that I once endured (in romance or in growing up).

Smart people learn from the bad and do what it takes to keep it from happening again. Can you be that smart?

- I'm afraid of having financial difficulties if we commit.

Make sure all finances are in order with both people before you do. Then make ground rules for finances before you commit to each other.

- I'm afraid of being a parent.

Look at all the people in the world. All of us had parents. Most of us turn out pretty good no matter what mistakes our parents made. So will your children if you love them.

- It scares me to be in any relationship I cannot walk away from anytime I want to.

In reality, we have little control over any portion of our lives and only think we do when we remain isolated and aloof. Life is much easier with a loving partner than when alone.

If you develop a relationship that begins to get serious, talk about the above list with the other person to find what s/he thinks about each of these fears. Ask what other fears s/he can think of that keep people from committing, and then talk about those. Listen very carefully to what the person is telling you about him-herself.

There is no fear in love. But perfect love drives out fear, because fear has to do with punishment. The one who fears is not made perfect in love. (1 John 4:18)

In Conclusion

There is much more to attachment. We urge you to read chapter five in *Your LovePath* and watch the corresponding DVD together.

In the chapter in *Your LovePath,* you will see many more things about attachment, particularly the four glues that hold a relationship together and how to fulfill each other in body, mind, heart, and soul. These are important and deserve to be discussed by you and the person with whom you are in a relationship.

Moving On

After the next section **Daily Thoughts and Prayers** are questions that you need to answer before coming to the next class session. Please make sure you write your answers to those before coming to class.

Daily Thoughts and Prayers

Day One
Spend a few minutes meditating and talking with God about Psalm 15:1-5. Jot your thoughts here.

The one thing that I will make sure I pray about today that will help me always keep my word is....

Day Two
Spend a few minutes meditating and talking with God about times in your life when you failed to keep your word. Jot your thoughts here.

The one thing that I will make sure I pray about today that will help me always keep my word is....

Day Three

Spend a few minutes meditating and talking with God about times in your life when you kept your word even though it was painful to do so. Jot your thoughts here.

The one thing that I will make sure I pray about today that will help me always keep my word is....

Day Four

Spend a few minutes meditating and talking with God about His grace and mercy for you, even when you stumbled or didn't do as you should have. Jot your thoughts here.

The one thing that I will make sure I pray about today that will help me always keep my word is....

Day Five

Spend a few minutes meditating and talking with God about what you need from Him to live your life as one who keeps his or her word. Jot your thoughts here.

The one thing that I will make sure I pray about today that will help me always keep my word is....

Class Sharing Time

In your next group meeting, you will spend a few minutes sharing with your group. Before coming to class, think these through and write your answers. What we think and write about has dramatically more effect on us than what we talk about. Write your answers so that you get the most from this study.

1. (For couples) Think about the concept of "leave, cleave, and weave." What is a way you have tried to "leave, cleave, and weave" in your marriage?

    (For singles) Think about the concept of "leave, cleave, and weave." What are some of the things you would do in order to weave a life with your future spouse?

2. Was there a time that you kept a promise, even though it hurt? Explain. What did you learn from that experience?

3. Why do people in our society feel that they can break their marriage vows and end their marriages?

4. What would you want your children to understand and integrate into their lives about commitment?

5. What do you commit to do about your marriage (or if you were married) to both God and your mate?

Notes as you watch the DVD

If you know a marriage in crisis......

Maybe your marriage needs help. Maybe the marriage of someone you love needs help. Since 1999 our three-day intensive workshop has a success rate of 77% in turning marriages around and saving them.

We can help by God's grace. We want to help. We invite you to enroll in LovePath 911.

WHAT IS LOVEPATH 911?

LovePath 911 (LP911) is an intense turnaround weekend for marriages that are struggling or in trouble.

WHAT HAPPENS IN LOVEPATH 911?

In addition to the LovePath model, LP911 consists of several segments, each building on the one before. Segments include:

- assessing your relationship as it is now
- discovering how to stop hurting each other
- gaining revealing insight into yourself
- analyzing what would truly fulfill you in life, individually and/or as a couple
- dealing with anger
- overcoming hurt and pain
- learning new communication methods
- requiring and receiving respect
- forgiving
- achieving win/win solutions that make each of you happy
- understanding and mastering personality conflicts
- understanding and overcoming extramarital affairs
- solving sexual conflict or discontent
- and more.

IS THIS WORKSHOP A TYPE OF COUNSELING OR THERAPY?

Though workshop leaders typically have advanced degrees in psychiatry, psychology, or marriage and family therapy, this workshop is *not* counseling or therapy. It actually works on a different – remarkably different – level. That's why many counselors and therapists send couples to the workshop. It's also why many couples that have not had success in counseling or therapy come to us.

HOW SUCCESSFUL IS LOVEPATH 911?

Since 1999, three of four couples who attend save their marriages. That holds true even if one or both do *not* wish to be there or to save their marriages. Some come to ease their consciences. Others come to make their children, parents, friends, or ministers happy. Some come with full intention of leaving their spouse for their lover and come only to get a better deal in the divorce. No matter the reason they come, our success rate is still 3 of 4 couples.

What if one of us is in love with someone else?

Quite a few couples attend LP911 while one or both partners are in love with someone else. So why would you come if one or both love someone else?

1. If children are involved, you need to find a way to get along with each other even if you divorce.

2. You'll have a clearer conscience if you take at least three days to examine your current marriage before you leave it.

3. You may discover that there is an unknown, but very real factor that is affecting your view of your spouse and of your lover. Regardless of your ultimate decision, knowledge of this hidden factor will benefit you greatly.

4. You will have a better future – even if you divorce – if you learn why this marriage failed and what to do to make sure you never fail again.

5. The best reason of all is that though you may not be able to imagine it – and think that you don't even want it – you may learn to fall in love with each other again and have a wonderful future together.

WHAT IF I WANT TO COME BUT MY SPOUSE DOESN'T?

It's not unusual that one mate wants to come to LP911 but the other does not. If you would like more information on how you may get your spouse to come, email us at help@JoeBeam.com and we will email you a short document that will help.

Call us toll free at 866-903-0990 to learn more about this workshop and how God may use it to turn your marriage completely around and make it what you have always wanted it to be...

Chapter 6 – The Dynamics of Difference

Understanding why your partner is so weird sometimes...

> There are different kinds of gifts, but the same Spirit. There are different kinds of service, but the same Lord. There are different kinds of working, but the same God works all of them in all men. (1 Corinthians 12:4-6)

Be sure to read the chapter in *Your LovePath* and watch the DVD before doing these exercises. If you do not, these may be more confusing than helpful.

Biblical View of Differences in People

You have seen it in the Bible. Various people behave in different ways. Peter made rash decisions. Paul became angry quickly and made it evident that he was. John did not loudly voice his allegiance to Jesus as did Peter, but would not leave His side even in the worst of circumstances. Thomas operated from logic and wanted more facts. In this chapter, you will see how each of these people fit into the temperament model and how our communication with each person works best when we speak "their language" based on their temperament.

The classifications we provide from the passages below will not make sense to you unless you have read chapter six in *Your LovePath*. If you have not read it, stop and read it now. As you read about temperaments such as Commander, Calculator, Completer, and Communicator, turn back to this page to see how they illustrate in the actions of these people from the Bible.

Paul behaved primarily in the temperament of a Commander. Note these passages that demonstrate his commander temperament.

- **Strong, direct statements:** *Would that those who are troubling you would even mutilate themselves.* (Galatians 5:12)

- **Responds to attacks with strength:** *Now some have become arrogant, as though I were not coming to you. But I will come to you soon, if the Lord wills, and I shall find out, not the words of those who are arrogant, but their power. For the kingdom of God does not consist in words, but in power. What do you desire? Shall I come to you with a rod or with love and a spirit of gentleness?* (1 Corinthians 4:18-21)

- **Determined to reach his goal, no matter what**: *And now, behold, bound in spirit, I am on my way to Jerusalem, not knowing what will happen to me there, except that the Holy Spirit solemnly testifies to me in every city, saying that bonds and afflictions await me. But I do not consider my life of any account as dear to myself, in order that I may finish my course, and the ministry which I received from the Lord Jesus, to testify solemnly of the gospel of the grace of God. And now, behold, I know that all of you, among whom I went about preaching the kingdom, will see my face no more. Therefore I testify to you this day that I am innocent of the blood of all men. For I did not shrink from declaring to you the whole purpose of God.* (Acts 20:22-26)

Thomas behaved primarily in the temperament of a Calculator. Note these passages that demonstrate his calculator temperament.

- **Faced life without letting emotion deter him**: *He said to the disciples, "Let us go to Judea again." The disciples said to Him, "Rabbi, the Jews were just now seeking to stone You, and are You going there again?"… "Our friend Lazarus has fallen asleep; but I go, that I may awaken him out of sleep." The disciples therefore said to Him, "Lord, if he has fallen asleep, he will recover." Now Jesus had spoken of his death, but they thought that He was speaking of literal sleep. Then Jesus therefore said to them plainly, "Lazarus is dead, and I am glad for your sakes that I was not there, so that you may believe; but let us go to him." Thomas therefore, who is called Didymus, said to his fellow disciples, "Let us also go, that we may die with Him."* (John 11:7-16)

- **Needed details and proof before making a decision**: *But Thomas, one of the twelve, called Didymus, was not with them when Jesus came. The other disciples therefore were saying to him, "We have seen the Lord!" But he said to them, "Unless I shall see in His hands the imprint of the nails, and put my finger into the place of the nails, and put my hand into His side, I will not believe." And after eight days again His disciples were inside, and Thomas with them. Jesus came, the doors having been shut, and stood in their midst, and said, "Peace {be} with you." Then He said to Thomas, "Reach here your finger, and see My hands; and reach here your hand, and put it into My side; and be not unbelieving, but believing."* (John 20:24-27)

John behaved primarily in the temperament of a Completer.

- **Completely loyal, staying with Jesus even in the face of possible death from those who knew he was with Jesus**: [Note that John is the "other disciple."] *Now Caiaphas was the one who had advised the Jews that it was expedient for one man to die on behalf of the people. And Simon Peter was following Jesus, and so was another disciple. Now that disciple was known to the high priest, and entered with Jesus into the court of the high priest, but Peter was standing at the door outside. So the other disciple, who was known to the high priest, went out and spoke to the doorkeeper, and brought in Peter.* (John 18:14-16)

- **Dedicated to the point that Jesus told him to care for Mary as if she were his own mother**: [John is the disciple whom Jesus loved.] *When Jesus therefore saw His mother, and the disciple whom He loved standing nearby, He said to His mother, "Woman, behold, your son!" Then He said to the disciple, "Behold, your mother!" And from that hour the disciple took her into his own household.* (John 19:26-27)

- **Family oriented, even with those he taught:** [Notice his language as he addresses them] *My little children, I am writing these things to you that you may not sin…Beloved, I am not writing a new commandment to you, but an old commandment which you have had from the beginning.* (1 John 2:1-7)

Peter behaved primarily in the temperament of a Communicator.

- **Impulsive:** *Peter…said, "Lord, if it is You, command me to come to You on the water." And He said, "Come!" And Peter got out of the boat, and walked on the water and came toward Jesus.* (Matthew 14:28-29)

- **Talks when he should keep quiet:** *Peter took Him aside and began to rebuke Him, saying, "God forbid it, Lord! This shall never happen to You." But He turned and said to Peter, "Get behind Me, Satan! You are a stumbling block to Me; for you are not setting your mind on God's interests, but man's."* (Matthew 16:22-23)

- **Fearing rejection, he makes promises that he cannot keep:** *Peter…said to Him, "Even though all may fall away because of You, I will never fall away." Jesus said to him, "Truly I say to you that this very night, before a cock crows, you shall deny Me three times." Peter said to Him, "Even if I have to die with You, I will not deny You."* (Matthew 26:33-35)

As mentioned earlier, turn back to these pages as you work through the exercises below. These men from the Word demonstrate the differences in people, as well as showing that we can work together in love even when our temperaments differ.

The Four Temperaments Graphed

There are four temperaments discussed in chapter six of *Your LovePath*. By temperament, we mean the characteristics of a person in the way s/he thinks, behaves, and reacts. In the book, you will see the four-quadrant model that helps us understand the temperaments.

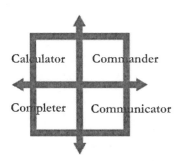

Those above the horizontal line tend to be cool and distant – sometimes standoffish, a little harder to get to know. Those below the horizontal line tend to be warm and friendly, easier to get to know.

Those to the left of the vertical line tend to process and then act. That means they think before deciding what to do. Those to the right of the vertical line tend to act and then process. That means that they react quickly, usually without stopping to think things through first.

Determining a Person's Temperament

The first thing to decide about the person is whether s/he is one who processes before acting or one who acts before processing. Is this person fast or slow in responding to the conversation of others? The second is whether this person tends to be cool and distant or warm and friendly. When people meet this person, would they think him/her cool or warm? Put together the answers and you have a theory as to which quadrant s/he goes in.

- Cool & Distant + Act Then Process = **Commander**

- Cool & Distant + Process Then Act = **Calculator**

- Warm & Friendly + Process Then Act = **Completer**

- Warm & Friendly + Act Then Process = **Communicator**

The following chart may help. **Note:** Nearly everyone has a combination of temperaments. Figure out the dominant one, and when another is strong, which is the secondary one. Count how many descriptors apply to the person you are evaluating. The totals for each temperament may give you better insight.

Commander	Calculator	Completer	Communicator
Strong ego	Practical	Laid back	Likes attention
Surrounds self with things that show fame, success, or power	Surrounds self with order, everything in its place	Surrounds self with things that are comfortable or family oriented	Surrounds self with fun things, usually cluttered
Impatient	Detailed	Thoughtful	Impulsive
Tells others what to do	Wants everyone to follow the rules	High importance on loyalty	Wants everyone happy
Does not want many details, just bottom line	Wants all relevant information available	Thinks carefully with available information	May forget details and act on emotion
Direct – may be considered rude	Factual – may be considered dry	Loyal to those who matter to him/her	Talkative and sometimes rambles
Solves problems quickly and sometimes harshly	Solves problems by evaluating, examining	Solves problems by avoiding, if possible	Solves problems with a group, often appeasing
Dominating	No Nonsense	Easy going	Outgoing
Results focused	Facts focused	Process focused	People focused
Competitive	Logical	Seen as wise	Impulsive

WHAT IS YOUR TEMPERAMENT

Now fill in the blank, "I think I may be a _____." This could be a combination of primary and secondary, such as "I think I may be a Communicator/Commander."

To get another view, ask two or more people who know you well to go through the exercise and tell you what they think you are.

If You Are Married

Most people who are in relationships are in that relationship with a person of differing temperament. Therefore, do not panic if your partner's temperaments are very different from yours. It will take more work, but thousands and thousands of couples do it well.

After each of you has completed the exercises above, compare your views of yourselves and each other. Share what you think with each other and then complete the questions below.

WHAT ARE MY CHARACTERISTICS?

WHAT ARE MY SPOUSE'S CHARACTERISTICS?

"It seems that I am a _____."

"It seems that my loved one is a _____."

HOW YOUR TEMPERAMENTS AFFECT YOUR MARRIAGE

There is no temperament better than another and no combination of primary and secondary temperaments that are better than others. You are what you are. Remember what Peter said in Acts 10:34-35: *"I now realize how true it is that God does not show favoritism but accepts men from every nation who fear him and do what is right."*

As we covered in chapter three, acceptance is the key to love. Do not try to make your spouse into something s/he is not. Neither should you let your spouse try to make you into something that you are not. The secret here is not to change one's temperament, but to find a way to have a good relationship when your temperaments conflict.

Using the temperaments as your basis, answer the following questions together. Talk them through. Do not be pushy and do not be defensive. The goal is not to convince, but to cooperate.

(Some of the questions may not apply to your marriage.)

1. Based on our temperaments, how do we differently approach finances?

2. Based on our temperaments, how do we differently approach parenting?

3. Based on our temperaments, how do we differently approach sex?

4. Based on our temperaments, how do we differently approach consulting each other before making decisions?

5. Based on our temperaments, how do we differently approach dealing with conflict?

If You Are Not In a Relationship

After you have completed the exercises about yourself in the Determining Temperaments section above, read chapter six in *Your LovePath* to discover with which temperaments you likely would interact best. This does not mean that you cannot have a good relationship with a person of a very different temperament; however, it is easier to have a good relationship with a person who is more like you. It takes more work – especially compromise – to have a good relationship with a person who is less like you.

After reading chapter six, list here the temperaments that would blend most easily with yours:

As you meet people who may be potential companions, early in the relationship use the two questions in the Determining Temperaments section to get a theory about which quadrant s/he is in, both primary and secondary. Watch that person's actions and expressed attitudes to determine if your initial analysis was correct.

When you feel that you have read this person correctly, ask yourself the following questions before getting serious. If you wait until you are already serious, you will not be objective.

1. How would our respective temperaments affect our relationship in the future?

2. How much work would it take for each of us to be happy with our respective temperaments if we made a commitment to each other?

3. What would I have to be aware of to best get along with this person?

4. What changes or adjustments would I have to make to my own behavior to have a good relationship with this person?

5. What would this person have to be aware of to best get along with me?

6. What changes or adjustment to this person's behaviors would need to take place for him/her to get along with me?

7. Is developing this relationship worth all it will take to make it good?

Honestly evaluate each of these if you wish to choose wisely.

Daily Thoughts and Prayers

Day One

Spend a few minutes meditating and talking with God about your personality and how you believe He thinks of you. Jot your thoughts here.

The one thing that I will make sure I pray about today that will help me be a loving person is...

Day Two

Spend a few minutes meditating and talking with God about your spouse's personality, especially those things you are thankful for about him or her. (If you are single, spend time with God about what you want your spouse's personality to be.) Jot your thoughts here.

The one thing that I will make sure I pray about today that will help me be a loving person is...

Day Three

Spend a few minutes meditating and talking with God about how you could use your personality to serve Him more than you ever have before. Jot your thoughts here.

The one thing that I will make sure I pray about today that will help me be a loving person is...

Day Four

Spend a few minutes meditating and talking with God about anything in your personality that you wish to change. Jot your thoughts here.

The one thing that I will make sure I pray about today that will help me be a loving person is...

Day Five

Spend a few minutes meditating and talking with God thanking Him for making you with the strengths and assets that He did. Talk those over with Him one at a time. Jot your thoughts here.

The one thing that I will make sure I pray about today that will help me be a loving person is...

Class Sharing Time

In your next group meeting, you will spend a few minutes sharing with your group. Before coming to class, think these through and write your answers. What we think and write about has dramatically more effect on us than what we talk about. Write your answers so that you get the most from this study.

1. (For couples) Understanding the temperaments of yourself and your spouse, what is one thing you can do to improve your communication/interaction?

   (For singles) Understanding your temperament, what is one thing you can do to better express your feelings with those closest to you?

2. Study the list of characteristics given for your personality type. Which do you find the most positive? The least positive?

3. Other than the examples given in the workbook, what Bible character do you think you are similar to? Why?

4. (For couples) What is your favorite thing about your spouse's temperament?

   (For singles) Which temperament do you think would best compliment your own?

5. If there was one thing you wish God would give you the ability to change about yourself, what would it be? Why?

Notes as you watch the DVD

Invite Joe Beam to speak....

Invite Joe Beam to your church or organization for a one-day marriage event, or an entire weekend…

TWO WAYS TO BOOK....

You may book Joe for a Saturday, or, if you wish, for a Sunday through Monday or Tuesday.

- If you choose the one-day event, the seminar is from 9 a.m. to 4 p.m. with a 1 ½ break for lunch.

- If you choose the weekend package, Joe speaks for your church Sunday morning, then does a 1 ½ to 2 hour Sunday evening presentation, and 2 to 2 ½ hour Monday evening presentation.

Whatever timing or format you book, Joe always includes the LovePath model. The rest of the segments are optional; choose the ones best suited for you group.

THE PERSONALITIES OF MARRIAGE

A fun and practical look at the way personalities affect marriage. Did Chapter 6 in the Your LovePath book and this workbook leave you wanting to know more? In this 1 ½ hour session Joe explains in greater detail. While often hilarious, the information is very much needed and oh so valuable to every couple. It also helps in parenting!

SEX IN MARRIAGE

An optional 2 ½ section, this section discusses sex in marriage from a Biblical and scientific perspective. Joe deals with basic knowledge, common problems, and God-given principles for a wonderful and fulfilling sex life in marriage. The last hour is a question and answer period where Joe answers questions submitted in writing from anonymous audience members. *Be aware that this is a very frank discussion and that he questions asked are often very specific. Don't be surprised to hear questions about pornography, masturbation, oral sex, anal sex, and more.*

SOLVING INSOLVABLE PROBLEMS IN MARRIAGE

An optional 1 ½ hour session, this very practical segment leads couples through a process of understanding what their true core issues are when they have an apparently insolvable problem. After teaching a technique to identify core issues, Joe then leads them through a simple, yet powerful method for finding compromise that both will be pleased with.

CALL 866-903-0990 FOR DETAILS AND MORE AVAILABLE SEGMENTS.

Chapter 7 – A Relationship in Retreat

Understanding what takes you the wrong way on the LovePath...

Now Sarai, Abram's wife, had borne him no children. But she had an Egyptian maidservant named Hagar; so she said to Abram, "The LORD has kept me from having children. Go, sleep with my maidservant; perhaps I can build a family through her." Abram agreed to what Sarai said. So after Abram had been living in Canaan ten years, Sarai his wife took her Egyptian maidservant Hagar and gave her to her husband to be his wife. He slept with Hagar, and she conceived. When she knew she was pregnant, she began to despise her mistress. Then Sarai said to Abram, "You are responsible for the wrong I am suffering. I put my servant in your arms, and now that she knows she is pregnant, she despises me. May the LORD judge between you and me." (Genesis 16:1-5)

U nfortunately, many couples believe their relationship will last forever and do not see the signs when their relationship deteriorates.

If you are not married, this chapter will not apply to you now, but will be of great value when you enter a relationship.

If you are married, our goal is to help you understand and be aware of those things that could negatively affect your relationship. Maybe some of them already exist.

Biblical View of Maintaining Marriage

Most Bible-reading folks know that God wants marriages to stay together. No matter how much one may wish to justify divorcing a mate, the Bible continues to contain passages such as:

- *And this is another thing you do: you cover the altar of the LORD with tears, with weeping and with groaning, because He no longer regards the offering or accepts it with favor from your hand. Yet you say, "For what reason?" Because the LORD has been a witness between you and the wife of your youth, against whom you have dealt treacherously, though she is your companion and your wife by covenant. But not one has done so who has a remnant of the Spirit. And what did that one do while he was seeking a godly offspring? Take heed then, to your spirit, and let no one deal treacherously against the wife of your youth. "For I hate divorce," says the LORD, the God of Israel, "and him who covers his garment with wrong," says the LORD of hosts. "So take heed to your spirit, that you do not deal treacherously."* (Malachi 2:13-16)

- o God bluntly demonstrates in this passage His unhappiness with the worship of those who "deal treacherously" with their companions and mates by covenant.

  - ▪ Marriage is a covenant before God.

  - ▪ A covenant is a formal agreement with legal and spiritual validity.

- o He says that those who have a remnant of the Spirit do not do this to their spouses.

- o In the strongest words He tells us that God hates divorce and warns that we should "take heed to our spirit, that [we] do not deal treacherously" with our spouses by divorcing.

- [Jesus teaches] *And it was said, "Whoever sends his wife away, let him give her a certificate of divorce"; but I say to you that everyone who divorces his wife, except for the cause of unchastity, makes her commit adultery; and whoever marries a divorced woman commits adultery.* (Matthew 5:31-32)

- *...some Pharisees came to Him [Jesus], testing Him, and saying, "Is it lawful for a man to divorce his wife for any cause at all?" And He answered and said, "Have you not read, that He who created them from the beginning made them male and female, and said, 'For this cause a man shall leave his father and mother, and shall cleave to his wife; and the two shall become one flesh'? Consequently they are no longer two, but one flesh. What therefore God has joined together, let no man separate." They said to Him, "Why then did Moses command to give her a certificate of divorce and send her away?" He said to them, "Because of your hardness of heart, Moses permitted you to divorce your wives; but from the beginning it has not been this way. And I say to you, whoever divorces his wife, except for immorality, and marries another woman commits adultery."* (Matthew 19:3-9)

- [Jesus said] *"...from the beginning of creation, God made them male and female. For this cause a man shall leave his father and mother, and the two shall become one flesh; consequently they are no longer two, but one flesh. What therefore God has joined together, let no man separate." And in the house the disciples began questioning Him about this again. And He said to them, "Whoever divorces his wife and marries another woman commits adultery against her; and if she herself divorces her husband and marries another man, she is committing adultery."* (Mark 10:6-12)

- [Paul writes] *But to the married I give instructions, not I, but the Lord, that the wife should not leave her husband (but if she does leave, let her remain unmarried, or else be reconciled to her husband), and that the husband should not send his wife away.* (1 Corinthians 7:10-11)

God is so intent on maintaining covenant that He uses a broken marriage as an illustration of how He viewed the nation of Israel when they broke their covenant with Him by leaving Him for the worship of idols.

- *Then the LORD said to me in the days of Josiah the king, "Have you seen what faithless Israel did? She went up on every high hill and under every green tree, and she was a harlot there. And I thought, 'After she has done all these things, she will return to Me'; but she did not return, and her treacherous sister Judah saw it. And I saw that for all the adulteries of faithless Israel, I had sent her away and given her a writ of divorce, yet her treacherous sister Judah did not fear; but she went and was a harlot also. And it came about because of the lightness of her harlotry, that she polluted the land and committed adultery with stones and trees." (Jeremiah 3:6-9)*

If we are to maintain marriages, not divorcing our mates, then we must do all it takes to keep our marriages together. The trouble is most people do not notice their relationship deteriorating until it becomes so bad that they strongly desire leaving each other to the point of seeking every excuse to justify their departure.

To keep that from happening to you, this chapter takes you through intense exercises to honestly evaluate where you are in your relationship, even to the point of admitting its weaknesses.

The Place to Start

WARNING: If you and your spouse are not communicating well and find yourselves often in arguments that lead to hurt, anger, or disappointment, go to chapter eight and do the exercises there before doing the exercises in this chapter.

Our goal in this chapter is to uncover for you and your partner anything causing either of you to move – knowingly or unknowingly – backward down the LovePath. We hope to help you find anything that happens or does not happen in your relationship.

- The <u>physical attraction</u> within the **Attraction** step refers to what you perceive the other person does for him- herself that either attracts or repulses you.

- The <u>physical fulfillment</u> within the **Attachment** step refers to what the person does for you that leads you to want either to stay or move away.

- As you answer each question, think not only in terms of what your spouse does, but also in terms of what s/he does not do.

- Later in this chapter, we will ask you to share the answers below with your spouse. We urge you to be absolutely open and honest, but we realize that may not be possible because of the nature of your relationship. If you cannot be open and honest, we strongly suggest that you evaluate your relationship. A relationship lacking openness and honesty never reaches the level of love the LovePath offers. If that is the case in your relationship, consider professional counseling.

➤ We realize that you will not study the **Aspiration** step until chapter nine. However, we ask questions about that step as well. We make those questions clear enough that you should be able to answer them.

Examining Attractiveness

Before answering the questions below, look over the ratings in chapter two.

1. Write everything about his/her physical appearance that is not as fulfilling to you as you wish. (For example, you may mention weight or physical condition, hygiene, dress, etc.) This should be your perception of what the person does for him- herself.

2. Write everything about his/her intellectual attraction that is not as fulfilling to you as you wish. (For example, it may be a lack of meaningful conversation, little interest in keeping up with information important to you, etc.)

3. Write everything about his/her emotional attraction that is not as fulfilling to you as you wish. (For example, it may be a lack of emotional safety, or a lack of opportunities to enjoy life with one another, etc.)

4. Write everything about his/her spiritual attraction that is not as fulfilling to you as you wish. (For example, it may be a conflict in important beliefs and values, disagreement about religion, disappointment with morality, etc.)

Examining Acceptance

Before answering the questions below, briefly look over acceptance in chapter three.

1. Write anything about his/her acceptance of you that is not as fulfilling to you as you wish. (For example, s/he does not accept your feelings about his/her parents, rejects your emotions as invalid, constantly criticizes you and tells you how to do things differently, etc.)

2. Write everything about him/her that you find difficult to accept as s/he wishes you to accept. (For example, it may be a habit, the way s/he talks to you, feeling left out of things, etc.)

3. Write everything about every hurt you have from this relationship. (For example, feeling unaccepted as the person rather than the picture s/he wants you to paint, hurt from feeling mistreated, hurt from feeling that s/her does not listen to you, etc.)

Examining Attachment

Before answering the questions below, briefly look over chapter five about attachment. Remember, this section is what the person does for you.

1. Write anything about his/her failure to meet your physical needs. (For example, it might be sexual fulfillment, helping you get in shape, etc.)

2. Write everything about his/her failure to meet your intellectual needs. (For example, it may be having a daily conversation, taking a class together to learn how to invest money, etc.)

3. Write everything about his/her failure to meet your important emotional needs. (For example, wanting more demonstrated affection, hearing often his/her love for you, surprising you with gifts, etc.)

4. Write everything about his/her failure to meet your spiritual needs. (For example, not praying with your or your children, not learning spiritual matters together, not attending religious service with you, not living by your moral standards, etc.)

Examining Aspiration

You have not reached the point in the book or workbook to prepare you for these questions. Answer as best you can.

1. Write everything about his/her rejection of – or ignoring of – the goals and dreams you have for your life. (For example, it may be that you want children and s/he does not, you wish to be a teacher and s/he berates that profession, you wish to have a close-knit family home every evening but s/he wants to travel, etc.)

2. Write everything about his/her not cooperating with you as you attempt to achieve those things important to you. (For example, it may be that you want him/her to do more around the home so that you can go back to school but s/he refuses, you wish to get a different job but s/he derides the very thought, you wish to learn to play the piano and s/he ridicules that, etc.)

Talking it out

If you feel your relationship can handle it, the best thing you can do is discuss what each of you wrote in answer to all the questions above.

Give each other immunity to tell the entire truth. That means that you promise not to hold against the other person anything that s/he tells you as s/he shares answers with you. The person telling the truth should do so with love and tact – *"A word aptly spoken is like apples of gold in settings of silver."* (Proverbs 25:11)

If either of you becomes emotional – especially angry – stop the exercise and do not attempt it again until each of you has complete control of your emotions.

Together, go back over every question in this chapter and share your answers. One goes first – toss a coin if necessary – and answers all the questions under that step of the LovePath. As one shares, the other listens without comment or negative body language. Instead, s/he makes notes. When that person finishes sharing all his/her answers to the questions, the other person follows the below steps.

1. Ask for clarification on anything said by the other. This must not be defensive, angry, dismissive, sarcastic, or anything of the kind. It must genuinely be for clarification, nothing more.

2. Ask how important each answer is to the person on a scale of 1 to 10. One is of little importance – a minor nuisance; ten is a potential deal breaker that puts your relationship in jeopardy.

3. Ask that person what s/he feels would repair any dissatisfaction, unhappiness, frustration, or lack of fulfillment. Write down what the person suggests.

4. Discuss possible solutions to anything that rates five or higher on the importance scale. Try to find one on which you both agree without reservation. Do not try to convince the other person to do anything; it must be by mutual enthusiastic agreement.

5. Agree on a path for solution and try it together.

When one person finishes answering all the questions under a particular heading – such as attractiveness – the other then shares all his/her answers. Be aware that this may not happen on the same day. Take your time. Finishing rapidly has no comparison to finishing well. Discuss everything clearly and with compassion.

In Conclusion

This chapter could be painful and therefore you may have decided to skip it and come back to it later, if at all. That is your privilege. However, if you do not open your eyes, and the eyes of each other, you may find that at least one of you has backtracked down the LovePath. Please consider that and face reality as it is rather than fantasy as you hope it to be.

Moving On

After the next section **Daily Thoughts and Prayers** are questions that you need to answer before coming to the next class session. Please make sure you write your answers to those before coming to class.

Daily Thoughts and Prayers

Day One

Spend a few minutes meditating and talking with God about how to be a great spouse for a lifetime. Jot your thoughts here. (If you are single, this same meditation and prayer applies to your future if you ever intend to marry….)

The one thing that I will make sure I pray about today that will help me be married for a lifetime is…

Day Two

Spend a few minutes meditating and talking with God about how to help your mate be a great spouse for a lifetime. Jot your thoughts here. (Singles, think of what you want to help your mate be.)

The one thing that I will make sure I pray about today that will help me be married for a lifetime is…

Day Three

Spend a few minutes meditating and talking with God about how many marriages end and how He feels about that. Jot your thoughts here.

The one thing that I will make sure I pray about today that will help me be married for a lifetime is...

Day Four

Spend a few minutes meditating and talking with God about the grace, mercy, understanding, and acceptance that you give your spouse. Jot your thoughts here. (Singles, about how you do these things with people that you love.)

The one thing that I will make sure I pray about today that will help me be married for a lifetime is...

Day Five

Meditate today about what you love about yourself—not arrogantly or in vain—but in true evaluation of self... Jot your thoughts here.

The one thing that I will make sure I pray about today that will help me be married for a lifetime is...

Class Sharing Time

In your next group meeting, you will spend a few minutes sharing with your group. Before coming to class, think these through and write your answers. What we think and write about has dramatically more effect on us than what we talk about. Write your answers so that you get the most from this study.

1. What are the reasons that marriages end? Think of as many as you can.

2. Which of those reasons you listed in question one could have been remedied if the couple had both been willing to work on the problem? How would they have solved each of those "marriage ending" reasons?

3. What do you think is the biggest factor in Christian divorces? Why?

4. (For couples) what is something you can do to strengthen your attraction to your spouse?

   (For singles) What is something you can do before you are married to strengthen your relationship with a potential mate?

5. What are some things you can do to become a safe place for others, especially your spouse, to tell the truth?

Notes as you watch the DVD

Chapter 8 – The Challenge of Conflict

Understanding how both of you can win...

What causes fights and quarrels among you? Don't they come from your desires that battle within you? (James 4:1)

I t is inevitable; there will be conflict in every relationship. We want things to go as we wish and, if that is important to us, we fight for our idea if the other person wants things to go another way.

Human nature. We all have it. Selfish? Not necessarily, though sometimes it may be.

This conflict only becomes a problem when the people involved allow their disagreement to turn into an argument that does not solve anything and causes anger, hurt, or disappointment.

If you are not in a relationship, this chapter may seem irrelevant to you. However, it is valuable to you now. Whether or not you are in a relationship with a fiancé, boyfriend, or girlfriend, you have relationships with others who are close to you. It may be your family, best friend, co-worker, etc. The principles in this chapter apply to all arguments. If you are in a relationship, this chapter definitely applies to you now.

Biblical View of Conflict

God recognizes that conflict occurs between human beings. No matter how spiritual, pure, or focused, we eventually find ourselves in disagreement with another. Conflict does not mean one (or both) is evil. It is not disagreement we are to avoid, but disagreements done in the wrong way.

When one allows him- herself to become angry in conflict, trouble results. God speaks to this throughout the Old Testament, telling us how to handle our anger and deal with conflict productively.

- **Do not allow your temper to flare**: *He who is slow to anger has great understanding, but he who is quick-tempered exalts folly.* (Proverbs 14:29)

- **Think carefully before responding to the one with whom you have conflict**: *A gentle answer turns away wrath, but a harsh word stirs up anger.* (Proverbs 15:1)

- **Control your anger when disagreeing and you can bring peace to the contention**: *A hot-tempered man stirs up strife, but the slow to anger pacifies contention.* (Proverbs 15:18)

- **Slow down and think before you speak:** *The heart of the righteous ponders how to answer, but the mouth of the wicked pours out evil things.* (Proverbs 15:28)

- **Wise people know when to forgive and move on:** *A man's discretion makes him slow to anger, and it is his glory to overlook a transgression.* (Proverbs 19:11)

- **Do not allow yourself to keep thinking about it (fret):** *Cease from anger, and forsake wrath; do not fret, it leads only to evildoing.* (Psalm 37:8)

The New Testament continues the teaching:

- **Do not allow your anger to lead you to sin; deal with it quickly and move on:** *Be angry, and yet do not sin; do not let the sun go down on your anger.* (Ephesians 4:26)

- **In your anger do not slander the person with whom you disagree. Instead be kind, tender-hearted, and learn to forgive:** *Let all bitterness and wrath and anger and clamor and slander be put away from you, along with all malice. And be kind to one another, tender-hearted, forgiving each other, just as God in Christ also has forgiven you.* (Ephesians 4:31-32)

- **Those who do not control anger do not "achieve the righteousness of God," and have a worthless religion. S/he deceives self by thinking him- herself righteous yet not controlling his/her hurtful language:** *...let everyone be quick to hear, slow to speak and slow to anger; for the anger of man does not achieve the righteousness of God...If anyone thinks himself to be religious, and yet does not bridle his tongue but deceives his own heart, this man's religion is worthless.* (James 1:19, 20, 26)

What happens to relationships in which conflict is not handled well? Consider this example in 2 Samuel. Michal, wife of King David, became enraged at his dancing in public, though David's intent was to dance before the Lord.

- She chastised him: *Michal...came out to meet David and said, "How the king of Israel distinguished himself today! He uncovered himself today in the eyes of his servants' maids as one of the foolish ones shamelessly uncovers himself!"* (2 Samuel 6:20)

- He defended his dancing and then told her that he would be humble in his own eyes but distinguished in the eyes of those maidens. In essence, he told her that other women – even servants – gave him more understanding and respect than his own wife.

- *And Michal...had no child to the day of her death.* (2 Samuel 6:23)

How do we keep that from happening to our marriages?

Watching for Triggers

If you find yourselves in arguments that do not solve disagreements but rather lead to anger, hurt, or disappointment, we provide the first step in reframing that process. Nearly all arguments of the type we discuss have a trigger that begins the conflict. A trigger is an action – either verbal or physical – that sets the other person off. When a trigger occurs, the argument proceeds in a line usually such as this:

trigger—disagreement/hurt/anger—argument—no mutually agreeable solution—bad feelings

The progression may be different with some couples, but it usually applies to all nonproductive arguments. Think back over arguments you have had, especially those that repeat, and figure out the trigger that usually starts the argument.

Write here triggers that you do which causes your spouse to feel anger or hurt.

Write here triggers that your spouse does which causes you to feel anger or hurt.

If you communicate well, share your answers. When the other person tells you your triggers, you must not become defensive, disagree that it is a trigger, react with anger, stop the communication, or any other negative thing. Listen to understand.

Everyone desires peace in a relationship and in life. By examining the triggers in your relationship, and working to remove them, you step closer to peace. Remember, no one wants to get caught up in nonproductive arguments: *Better to live on a corner of the roof than share a house with a quarrelsome wife [or husband!].* (Proverbs 25:24)

Win-Win Guidelines

We use the word guidelines instead of rules because it may be that a particular couple should modify the guidelines to fit their personalities and situations.

These guidelines assume the argument is not just to hurt the other person, but that each person has a desire, idea, action, etc., that s/he wants the other to accept, tolerate, or do. In short, these guidelines provide a method for finding a solution.

1. Make the environment safe for each of you, both physically and emotionally.

    a. Pick a location where neither of you will be self-conscious nor fear embarrassment. (For example, do not argue in a restaurant. Wait until you are in an emotionally safer place.)

    b. Choose the right time. (For example: do not begin an argument when one of you must leave soon for an appointment or work.)

2. Operate within issue boundaries – deal with the issue at hand.

    a. Do not bring up any current issues that are not directly related.

    b. Do not bring up any past issue unless that is all you are discussing.

3. Seek to understand before being understood.

    a. Do not argue your point strongly at the outset. If you do, the other person may yield, not because of mutual agreement, but to cease the conflict. That nearly always results in resentment.

    b. Listen carefully for the other person's point of view. You may discover it is not too different from your own if you truly listen to what the other person wants to accomplish.

4. Use non-judgmental brainstorming.

    a. Using the knowledge of each other's position (gained in step three), together brainstorm potential solutions in which each of you "wins." (If your argument is over opposing ideas, the win may be that each of you accepts that the other person sees it differently but that you will not let it negatively affect your relationship.)

    b. Ensure that no brainstormed idea is countered by sarcasm, derision, defensiveness, or any other negative. Make sure that each of you gets respect for every idea, no matter how foreign it seems to the other.

5. Find a mutually agreed upon solution.

    a. Do not cease searching for a solution until each enthusiastically agrees.

    b. To please both of you, choose a possible brainstormed solution that you both enthusiastically agree will provide a "win" for both of you.

6. Implement the mutually agreed upon solution.

    a. When you find a solution on which both of you enthusiastically agree, together make a plan to employ that solution.

    b. Agree to the plan when it begins, and honor that agreement.

7. Alter the solution as needed.

    a. If the agreed upon solution does not work to resolve the issue, discuss it to discover why.

    b. Go backwards through the seven steps, one at a time, to find the alteration that you need to make to have a mutually acceptable solution.

Together examine the above suggested guidelines. If you wish to alter any of the guidelines, remove one, or add one, please do so if that step works best for you as a couple.

Forgiving

There are actions or words from one partner that the other cannot get past easily. It may be something such as embarrassing the other in public. It may be an extramarital affair. We do not equate each of these actions, but we do wish to point out that forgiveness may be needed in any number of situations.

We listed three steps in *Your LovePath* that you should read again before completing the next exercise. These steps work well if you choose to forgive. Forgiveness is not an emotion; it is a decision. That decision will affect your emotions, though it may take time for it to do so. Be sure to check *Your LovePath* for the three steps.

Then Peter came and said to Him, "Lord, how often shall my brother sin against me and I forgive him? Up to seven times?" Jesus said to him, "I do not say to you, up to seven times, but up to seventy times seven." (Matthew 18:21-22)

List here the people you need to forgive and what they did that requires forgiveness.

Will you forgive? You may repeat the process below with many people, if necessary.

Name _____

1. Do you choose to decide that this person is not evil but a flawed human?

2. Do you choose to give up your right for vengeance (even if you have pursued vengeance until now)?

3. Do you choose to restore a relationship with this person? If so, write here what you need to do to restore that relationship, as well as anything you feel s/he needs to do to restore that relationship.

In Conclusion

Solving problems and finding happiness together is one of the most important skills required to maintain a relationship. Learn to do it well and a relationship can last for a lifetime.

Sometimes what one may consider a problem has to be solved by accepting and tolerating the ideas, beliefs, and opinions of another. That does not, of course, mean that you must tolerate his/her destructive behavior to self, you, ones you love, others, or even the relationship.

Rather than harboring anger or resentment, work together to solve all disagreements and problems.

Moving On

After the next section **Daily Thoughts and Prayers** are questions that you need to answer before coming to the next class session. Please make sure you write your answers to those before coming to class.

Daily Thoughts and Prayers

Day One

Spend a few minutes meditating and talking with God about things He has forgiven you for over the years. Jot your thoughts here.

The one thing that I will make sure I pray about today that will help me control my emotions, especially anger is…

Day Two

Spend a few minutes meditating and talking with God about things that you have forgiven others for over the years. How did your forgiving affect you? Jot your thoughts here.

The one thing that I will make sure I pray about today that will help me control my emotions, especially anger is…

Day Three

Spend a few minutes meditating and talking with God about things that trigger anger, resentment, or negative reactions in you. Jot your thoughts here.

The one thing that I will make sure I pray about today that will help me control my emotions, especially anger is...

Day Four

Spend a few minutes meditating and talking with God about things that trigger anger, resentment, or negative reactions in your spouse (or another person close to you.) Jot your thoughts here.

The one thing that I will make sure I pray about today that will help me control my emotions, especially anger is...

Day Five

Spend a few minutes meditating and talking with God about how you would like to act, be, and do when conflict comes into your life. Jot your thoughts here.

The one thing that I will make sure I pray about today that will help me control my emotions, especially anger is…

Class Sharing Time

In your next group meeting, you will spend a few minutes sharing with your group. Before coming to class, think these through and write your answers. What we think and write about has dramatically more effect on us than what we talk about. Write your answers so that you get the most from this study.

1. How do you handle conflict? What examples or experiences in life led you to handle conflict in this way?

2. What is a recurring conflict between you and your spouse/someone close to you? How can you resolve this conflict, once and for all?

3. What are some ways you calm your temper?

4. Forgiveness is a key element in conflict resolution. Is there anything that you have trouble feeling forgiven for? How does holding onto it feel? What would have to happen for you to feel forgiven?

5. What or whom do you have a problem forgiving? How could your small group help you learn to forgive?

Notes as you watch the DVD

Chapter 9 – Aspiration

Understanding the fulfillment of intimacy...

May he give you the desire of your heart and make all your plans succeed. (James 4:1)

We all have an aspiration for our lives. As you read chapter nine in *Your LovePath*, you saw an explanation of what we mean.

In *Your LovePath* we use the term Aspiration to refer to that which you want in your life. You may not be aware of your deepest aspiration or life desire. If you are, you may have abandoned it as hopeless, impractical, likely to be rejected by your partner, or selfish. However, to abandon a deeply held aspiration does not remove it from your heart and soul; because of your abandonment, it may lead to greater problems in your life and your relationship.

You will note that sometimes we use the word aspiration, at other times dream, and yet at other time life desire. In the context of this chapter, they all refer to the same thing.

If you are not in a relationship: This chapter is just as important to you as to those who are married. Most of what we share with those in a relationship applies to you, but additionally we provide an extra exercise for you later in this chapter.

If you are in a relationship: You may at first discount how important this principle is to your relationship. However, many couples have disagreements about something or other when in reality they are fighting over their unfulfilled dreams or life desires.

Biblical View of Aspiration

Be sure to read chapter nine in *Your LovePath* before going further in this workbook.

The Bible demonstrates clearly the power of a dream. Not a wish, but a true calling one feels on his or her life.

Perhaps the clearest story of this occurs in the life of Joseph.

> *"Please listen to this dream which I have had; for behold, we were binding sheaves in the field, and lo, my sheaf rose up and also stood erect; and behold, your sheaves gathered around and bowed down to my sheaf." Then his brothers said to him, "Are you actually going to reign over us? Or are you really going to rule over us?" So they hated him even more for his dreams and for his words. Now he had still another dream, and related it to his brothers, and said, "Lo, I have had still another dream; and behold, the sun and the moon and eleven stars were bowing down to me." And he related it to his father and to his brothers; and his father rebuked him and said to him, "What is this dream that you have had? Shall I and your mother and your brothers actually come to bow ourselves down before you to the ground?" And his brothers were jealous of him, but his father kept the saying in mind.* (Genesis 37:5-11)

Joseph believed this dream would come to realization and that belief affected everything he did — including endurance to all his trials — for the rest of his life. He never abandoned it, thought it foolish, or gave it up because of the doubt of others. Think of how his dream guided his life.

- His brothers ridiculed him, hating him, but he never wavered in his belief that he would accomplish his dream. (Genesis 37:5-11)

- His father, who loved him deeply, rebuked him for holding a dream that seemed arrogant. As much as he loved his father, Joseph did not falter. (Genesis 37:10)

- His brothers sold him into slavery. (Genesis 37:23-28) Anyone with common sense would know that a slave would never be a ruler. Yet Joseph preserved in believing his dream would come true.

- In Potiphar's house, Joseph became a leader, knowing that someday he would be a leader that even his parents would follow. His dream directed his future. (Genesis 39:1-6)

- "Mrs. Potiphar" attempted to seduce Joseph. Perhaps he could have justified yielding to her favors by considering how his family had turned against him. However, a man who genuinely believes he is destined to royalty would not allow himself to be tempted by anything that jeopardized his integrity or compromised his duty. (Genesis 39:7-13)

- Thrown into prison by Potiphar because of the lies of his spurned would-be lover, Joseph never faltered. If he had shared his dream with fellow prisoners, they would have laughed at his naivety and told him in strong language that slaves do not become kings. (Genesis 39:19-21)

  o Yet, his dream led him onward to the point that Joseph grew to a position of leadership within the prison.

  > *…the chief jailer committed to Joseph's charge all the prisoners who were in the jail; so that whatever was done there, he was responsible for it. The chief jailer did not supervise anything under Joseph's*

charge because the LORD was with him; and whatever he did, the Lord made to prosper. (Genesis 39:22-23)

- As we know from the end of the story, Joseph did become a ruler – just as his dream had always been – and his family did bow to him. Though they had thought his dream arrogant, they discovered it was the best thing that ever could have happened to them and their children.

…do not be grieved or angry with yourselves, because you sold me here; for God sent me before you to preserve life…to preserve for you a remnant in the earth, and to keep you alive by a great deliverance. Now, therefore, it was not you who sent me here, but God; and He has made me a father to Pharaoh and lord of all his household and ruler over all the land of Egypt. (Genesis 45:5-8)

His dream began during the seventeenth year of his life. It finally came to fulfillment in the thirtieth year. During thirteen years of misery – ridicule, rejection, slavery, prison – he always followed his dream.

A dream is far from a wish. It is a part of our identity, our purpose, and our fulfillment. When we have a dream, it diminishes our lives to forgo that dream, even if we do that for someone we love. If they are not completely selfish (everyone has some degree of selfishness, even Joseph), dreams are meant to be accomplished.

In marriage, you grow to the highest point on the LovePath – and the deepest level of love – if you assist each other in achieving your dreams.

Our Dreams

Therapist John Gottman at the University of Washington lists some common "deep" dreams or life desires. His list has 35 dreams. We list a few of them here.

- A sense of freedom
- Adventure
- Healing
- Having a sense of power
- Having a sense of order
- Travel

Often a person does not understand his/her life desire because s/he focuses on a mundane life desire that is easier to note. As Gottman writes, "For example, underneath the dream to make lots of money may be a deep need for security."

In *Your LovePath* we share the story of the book's author and his wife. They did not understand the deep meanings beneath their life desires because they focused on the "piggyback" life desires that they could understand. Read that story for more clarification.

Knowing & Understanding Your Deepest Aspiration

Looking deeper into yourself sometimes takes weeks or even months. Trying to finish it too fast may lead you to miss the underlying deep dreams altogether.

Think carefully and come to awareness of more easily discerned dreams that cause you disagreements or arguments. Particularly think of a repetitive disagreement that you have with each other that appears to have no possible solution.

Write here any and all arguments that occur repetitively between you and your spouse.

Examine your side of the argument to see what you argue for. Is it moving to another city? Quitting your job and taking one with more adventure but less income? Whatever it is, write here what you try to accomplish for yourself in these recurring arguments.

Examine what you wrote in the question above about your side of the argument. Dig deep into your mind, your emotions, and your intuition to answer this one question: What is the deep dream or desire within me that underlies what I argue for?

When you feel you know and understand your deepest desire, write it here. Spell it out in detail. Make it clear enough that others can comprehend it.

When both you and your spouse answer the previous question, share your deepest dream with each other. Even though this is not an argument, it is still communication in which you wish a win-win. Be sure that you employ the guidelines from chapter eight.

Write here the deep dream or desire that your spouse has. Write it in enough detail that when you return to it to read it later, you will grasp all of the meaning, emotion, and dedication s/he has to this aspiration.

Cooperating in Achieving Desires

Often couples find that their deepest desires conflict. How can he be free as a bird when she wants order and careful planning? How can one wish to travel the world when the other desires capturing the warmth of a home where everyone eats dinner together every night? The answer comes from learning to cooperate. Why do some people not want to do that? Some of the reasons are:

- Fear that if I help my partner achieve his/her dreams, mine will not be achieved

- Belief that my spouse has a dream that is unreasonable

- Resistance because my partner's dream contradicts my beliefs and values

Write here any reason that you find yourself hesitating to help your partner fulfill his/her dream or desire. Be honest with yourself.

Write here how you can overcome that hesitation.

To overcome these and other reasons that a person wishes not to cooperate, choose to find a way that each of you can fulfill your desire while helping the other fulfill his/her desires. Though that may seem impossible, approach it with the mindset that together you can find a way to do this. Follow the guidelines in chapter eight. Also:

- Do not try to persuade.

- Listen carefully to each other.

- The goal is to make sure that each of you will fulfill your deepest dreams.

- Each has to be a part of the other's dream and actively help it to come to realization.

- Do not settle on a potential solution until both of you enthusiastically agree.

- Note that the solution does not have to be one that will be accomplished quickly. It may be a solution that requires a plan that will take time to complete. That works well as long as both of you continue to work that plan.

- *If you have any encouragement from being united with Christ, if any comfort from his love, if any fellowship with the Spirit, if any tenderness and compassion, then make my joy complete by being like-minded, having the same love, being one in spirit and purpose. Do nothing out of selfish ambition or vain conceit, but in humility consider others better than yourselves. Each of you should look not only to your own interests, but also to the interests of others.* (Philippians 2:1-4)

Developing the Plan

When you reach a potential solution that both of you enthusiastically agree upon, write it here in detail.

Now together develop a plan for the implementation of this solution, making bullet points for each action required and a probable time for completion of that action. Remember, as long as both agree, it may stretch to months or years.

Write your plan, bullet points, actions, and times here.

Cooperating Over Time

Constantly monitor the implementation of your plan. If at any point either of you feels the plan is not going as expected or desired, you must together analyze what is not working well and how to correct it.

If it becomes clear the plan will not work, we suggest that together you back up one step at a time until you find the step where you can refocus. Then work down the steps again with that new focus.

If You Are Not in a Relationship

We strongly recommend that you work through the exercises above that apply to your knowing and comprehending your own deepest desires. The exercises about disagreements and arguments may not be of value to you now, but they will be if you enter into a relationship. It appears two people in a relationship hardly ever have the same deepest desire.

When you feel comfortable knowing and understanding your deepest life desire, use the following to evaluate any relationship that you develop. It may save quite a bit of misery down the line.

When dating seriously enough to talk about more intimate matters, begin a process to understand the person's deepest life desires. Share with him/her the section above about discovering and comprehending one's own life desires. Lead him/her through it until s/he is comfortable that s/he knows and understands his/her personal deepest dreams.

Use this checklist in considering a long-term future with this person.

1. Is the person's deepest dream compatible with yours or apparently incompatible?

2. Do you feel that you can accept and honor the person's deepest life desire to the point you will help him/her achieve it?

3. Did the person demonstrate respect for your deepest life desire and indicate that s/he would help you achieve it?

4. Are your respective dreams so different that it would take a great deal of compromise – perhaps emotionally draining – for each of you to achieve his/her deepest life desires?

5. Are you willing to put that much effort into developing a future with this person?

Discovering each other's deepest aspirations relatively early in a relationship can prevent conflict that would occur later. Remember that most couples argue over mundane life desires that disguise the deep dream under it. You can bypass those arguments by knowing, appreciating, and becoming part of each other's deepest life desires before making any commitment to each other.

In Conclusion

In *Your LovePath,* chapter nine also contains information about how to grow your relationship by helping each other achieve your aspirations.

We did not lead you through control exercises in this chapter because it is unlikely you can do the things above without relinquishing control and working in harmony. However, if you find that control is an issue:

1. Keep track of circumstances in which you felt the other was attempting to control you.

2. When you both are calm, share with the other the circumstance, what you felt, and why you felt it.

3. Ask the person if s/he realizes s/he was controlling in that circumstance. If so, ask why s/he felt the need to control.

4. Mutually agree that when you feel controlled you have the right to say that and the other person will stop that action and approach the subject in a loving, kind, and cooperative way.

Moving On

After the next section **Daily Thoughts and Prayers** are questions that you need to answer before coming to the next class session. Please make sure you write your answers to those before coming to class.

Daily Thoughts and Prayers

Day One
Spend a few minutes meditating and talking with God about your deepest life aspiration or dream. Jot your thoughts here.

The one thing that I will make sure I pray about today that will help me live the dream that I believe God has for me is…

Day Two
Spend a few minutes meditating and talking with God about why you have your deepest life aspiration or dream. Where did it come from? When did you first realize it? What does it mean to you? Jot your thoughts here.

The one thing that I will make sure I pray about today that will help me live the dream that I believe God has for me is…

Day Three

Spend a few minutes meditating and talking with God about whether your deepest life aspiration or dream is of God. Will it benefit His Kingdom? How? Do you believe that God gave you this dream or is He unhappy that you have this dream? Jot your thoughts here.

The one thing that I will make sure I pray about today that will help me live the dream that I believe God has for me is…

Day Four

Spend a few minutes meditating and talking with God about how He has prepared you to fulfill your deepest life aspiration or dream. What gifts did He give you? Talents? Education, both formal and from life? Jot your thoughts here.

The one thing that I will make sure I pray about today that will help me live the dream that I believe God has for me is…

Day Five

Spend a few minutes meditating and talking with God about what you should do NOW to fulfill your deepest life aspiration or dream. Jot your thoughts here.

The one thing that I will make sure I pray about today that will help me live the dream that I believe God has for me is...

Class Sharing Time

In your next group meeting, you will spend a few minutes sharing with your group. Before coming to class, think these through and write your answers. What we think and write about has dramatically more effect on us than what we talk about. Write your answers so that you get the most from this study.

1. What is your dream or aspiration for your life? Don't hesitate, feel it's silly, or analyze whether it's possible, just write down here what it is deep inside you?

2. Think deeply. What is it that your dream or life desire really means that you want? Look for the core issue. Try to see past the façade to the central element. Write your answer here if you can.

3. How has God gifted you for fulfilling that dream or life desire? What talents do you have? What have you learned in life that equips you?

4. Does something in your current life conflict with your deepest desire/aspiration? What steps can you take to overcome this conflict?

5. (For couples) Do you know your spouse's greatest aspiration? How can you help them achieve it?

   (For singles) How could a potential mate help you achieve your aspirations?

6. Recurring arguments are often symptoms of unrealized dreams and desires. Think about a recurring argument you have with your spouse/those closest to you. What steps can you take to end the argument and focus on the underlying aspiration?

Notes as you watch the DVD

Chapter 10 – Learning to Love More Deeply

Understanding how to use the LovePath for life...

Can two walk together, except they be agreed? (Amos 3:3)

It is time to see whether you traveled up the LovePath to greater love, remained stagnant in the same condition in which you started, or backtracked down the LovePath.

If you are not in a relationship, this chapter will have little value to you now. However, if early in your next relationship you do the exercises in chapter one, and you and your partner work through *Your LovePath* and this workbook, then complete chapter ten. By doing so, you will find how the LovePath grows your relationship.

Biblical View of Growing

We know that God wishes His children to grow to the level of highest purpose. Throughout scripture we watch the changing of people such as King David, Peter, Paul, and others.

We take time only to examine David's growth. He went through life starting as a "man after [the Lord's] own heart." (1 Samuel 13:14) He became a powerful warrior, evolving to a sinner of mammoth proportions (Psalm 51), and finally again to the man after God's own heart. Luke wrote of Jesus, *He will be great, and will be called the Son of the Most High; and the Lord God will give Him the throne of His father David.* (Luke 1:32) What greater honor could David receive from God Himself?

David grew. His relationship with God changed. He became a better person. God wants us to grow to maturity – especially spiritual maturity.

- *Yet we do speak wisdom among those who are mature; a wisdom, however, not of this age, nor of the rulers of this age, who are passing away.* (1 Corinthians 2:6)

- *Brethren, do not be children in your thinking; yet in evil be babes, but in your thinking be mature.* (1 Corinthians 14:20)

- *...until we all attain to the unity of the faith, and of the knowledge of the Son of God, to a mature man, to the measure of the stature which belongs to the fullness of Christ.* (Ephesians 4:13)

- *But solid food is for the mature, who because of practice have their senses trained to discern good and evil.* (Hebrews 5:14)

There is great value to measuring how one grows in spiritual maturity. However, that cannot be done with any degree of objectiveness unless criteria exist for evaluation. Various writers have tried to delineate which characteristics should be measured to evaluate spiritual growth. We do not enter that discussion here, but agree that some criteria must exist for the measurement of any growth and maturing.

Now that we established the Biblical principle of reaching maturity in relationship to God, we extrapolate that to growing in relationship with each other. God wants us to develop deep love for one another.

- *...until we all attain to the unity of the faith, and of the knowledge of the Son of God, to a mature man, to the measure of the stature which belongs to the fullness of Christ.* (Ephesians 4:13)

- *A new commandment I give to you, that you love one another, even as I have loved you, that you also love one another. By this all men will know that you are My disciples, if you have love for one another."* (John 13:34-35)

- *Let love be without hypocrisy. Abhor what is evil; cling to what is good. Be devoted to one another in brotherly love; give preference to one another in honor;* (Romans 12:9-10)

Do these "love" principles apply to marriage?

- **To Husbands:** *Husbands, love your wives, just as Christ also loved the church and gave Himself up for her; that...So husbands ought also to love their own wives as their own bodies. He who loves his own wife loves himself; for no one ever hated his own flesh, but nourishes and cherishes it, just as Christ also does the church...For this cause a man shall leave his father and mother, and shall cleave to his wife; and the two shall become one flesh...let each individual among you also love his own wife even as himself; and let the wife see to it that she respect her husband.* (Ephesians 5:25-33)

- **To Wives:** *Older women likewise are to be reverent in their behavior...teaching what is good, that they may encourage the young women to love their husbands, to love their children,* (Titus 2:3-4)

How would either spouse – male or female – evaluate whether love is growing, stagnant, or in retreat?

We offer one method in the remainder of this chapter.

Charting Growth

In chapter one, we asked you to complete the Kansas Marital Satisfaction survey. It may be that by now your scores differ from what they were then, because you both focus on following the LovePath. We ask you to take it again now.

Answer each question on a scale of 1 to 7.

1 = extremely dissatisfied
2 = very dissatisfied
3 = somewhat dissatisfied
4 = mixed
5 = somewhat satisfied
6 = very satisfied
7 = extremely satisfied

1. _____ How satisfied are you with your marriage?

2. _____ How satisfied are you with your relationship with your spouse?

3. _____ How satisfied are you with your husband/wife as a spouse?

Now add the three scores and divide by three to get an average score. _____

Subtract chapter one scores from your scores now.

Now =   6
Minus Chapter One =   4
Difference =   2

If the difference is a negative, list it as such. Example:

Now =   4
Minus Chapter One =   7
Difference =   -3

Put your scores in the table below:

	Chapter One	Now	Difference
1.			
2.			
3.			
Average			

The first measure of insight is to examine your Difference scores.

> ➤ If it is higher for a question or average, you are going the right direction on the LovePath.

> ➤ If it is zero for a question or average, you are not going up the LovePath but at least you are not going down the LovePath in the wrong direction.

> ➤ If it is lower for a question or average, you are going down the LovePath in what we refer to as backtracking.

More than examining your Difference scores, analyze any changes. Whether the scores increased, remained the same, or decreased, you should try to determine why. Was there a specific event? Has one of you changed? If so, which one? Or have you both changed? Have the exercises in this workbook made a difference? If so, good or bad?

An adage says that we can talk without thinking but that we cannot write without thinking. Therefore, as you analyze why your scores changed, write here the reasons you believe they did.

PLOT YOUR SCORES

If you and your spouse are communicating honestly and without negativity, use the following four quadrant model to discover where you are in your relationship now. Plot your average score from now on the graph below. Then plot your spouse's average score from now. The quadrant in which your scores intersect gives you a snapshot of where your relationship is now.

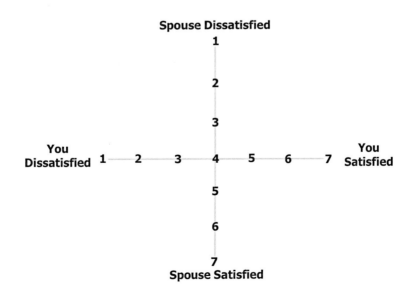

To see clearly how this graph works for the two of you, imagine that your average score is six while the other person's score is two. As shown on the next page, those scores intersect in the upper right quadrant.

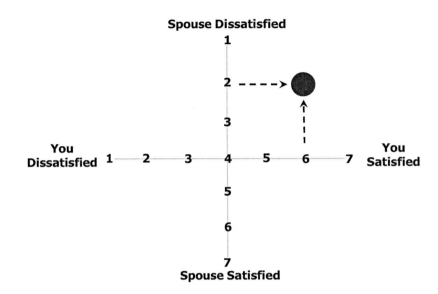

What do your intersecting scores indicate about your relationship?

In Conclusion

If you are not in a relationship, learn this path and follow it wisely in any relationship you develop.

If you are in a relationship: As indicated in *Your LovePath*, it may work for both parties in a relationship even if only one consciously follows the LovePath at the outset. *Your LovePath* also points out that if following the LovePath does not affect your partner as you wish, it is still the best thing you can do for you. You will never learn to love another as you should until you first love yourself.

Chapter ten in *Your LovePath* gives you more guidance. In this chapter of the workbook, we wanted only to show you how your relationship changed over the last ten sessions. We hope it grew in love. If it did not, it can. Follow the LovePath - thousands of couples proved that it works if one works it.

If we can be of assistance to you in your engagement or marriage, contact us at LovePath International, Inc.:

> ➢ If your marriage is in trouble, we can help with the intensive weekend *LovePath 911Workshop*. Since 1999 our success rate in saving crisis marriages and helping people learn to love again is three out of four couples. Even those who do not want their marriage to continue – or who are in love with someone else – have that success rate. Find out more by calling one of our crisis marriage consultants at **866.903.0990** or visit our web site at www.JoeBeam.com .

Daily Thoughts and Prayers

Day One

Spend a few minutes meditating and talking with God about His love for you. Jot your thoughts here.

The one thing that I will make sure I pray about today that will help me love more is....

Day Two

Spend a few minutes meditating and talking with God about your love for your spouse. Jot your thoughts here. (If single, about your love for the person that you love most.)

The one thing that I will make sure I pray about today that will help me love more is....

Day Three

Spend a few minutes meditating and talking with God about your spouse's love for you. Jot your thoughts here. (If single, about the love from the person that you love most.)

The one thing that I will make sure I pray about today that will help me love more is....

Day Four

Spend a few minutes meditating and talking with God about how to grow in love for your spouse for as long as you live. Jot your thoughts here. (If single, about how you would like to love when you marry, if you plan to marry.)

The one thing that I will make sure I pray about today that will help me love more is....

Day Five

Spend a few minutes meditating and talking with God about how you can use the principles of the LovePath to grow in your love for Him. Jot your thoughts here.

The one thing that I will make sure I pray about today that will help me love more is....

Class Sharing Time

In your next group meeting, you will spend a few minutes sharing with your group. Before coming to class, think these through and write your answers. What we think and write about has dramatically more effect on us than what we talk about. Write your answers so that you get the most from this study.

1. Examine the progress you have made through this study. Where do you think you have grown the most? The least?

2. What are some ways you can grow in spiritual maturity?

3. What potential "roadblocks" do you foresee as you follow the LovePath? How can these roadblocks be avoided or resolved?

4. How do you define love after this study?

5. What do you commit to do to grow on the LovePath with your spouse?

Notes as you watch the DVD

LovePath 911

If your marriage is in crisis—or if you love someone whose marriage is in crisis—our success rate since 1999 is three out of four marriages. It doesn't matter if one spouse comes reluctantly or under pressure. It doesn't matter if one is madly in love with someone else. Our success rate remains just as high. It is, of course, by the grace of God Almighty.

If you wish a miracle for you or someone you love, call now toll free 866-903-0990.

About Joe Beam

Joe Beam is Founder and Chairman of LovePath International, Inc., a corporation founded to guide people through the processes of love and specializing in saving marriages in crisis. Desiring to change the way couples live and love, he developed the LovePath system, a unique and highly effective methodology that combines a solid knowledge of relationship principles, human behavior, and group dynamics.

The author of several books, Beam has developed courses, seminars, and workshops attended by more than 120,000 people. He has been a guest on The Today Show, Good Morning America, The Montel Williams Show, Focus on the Family radio, The Dave Ramsey Show, and others. He has been in People magazine and Better Homes and Gardens magazine, as well as many newspapers and publications across America.

Book Joe Beam to speak at your church or organization...

Joe speaks on several topics related to love, sex, and marriage. You may book him for a Saturday seminar or a Sunday – Monday seminar. Though Joe always includes a section on the LovePath, you can pick and choose from several other topics for the remainder of the seminar. Several topics are available. The most popular are Joe's sessions on personalities and the very frank session on sex in marriage. However, you choose the topics most beneficial to your church or organization.

Call 866-903-0990 to get details.

Books by Joe Beam

Your Love Path Best-selling author and internationally respected marriage expert Joe Beam guides you through falling in love, growing in love, or, when necessary, rescuing lost love.

Seeing the Unseen: Preparing for Spiritual War In this national bestseller, Joe Beam reveals Satan's powerful weaponry - his lies, deceptions, and manipulations and unmasks his strategy to destroy your life and those you care for. This is not a book of wild sensationalism; rather, it is a dedicated study of God's Word.

The True Heaven This book is the expanded follow-up to The Real Heaven! It is an exciting and fast-paced book that deals with many topics of what Heaven will be like. This fascinating book uses the Bible to answer tough questions about Heaven and the next life.

Getting Past Guilt (Formerly known as Forgiven Forever) Forgiveness. The word itself fills our hearts with peace and hope. But countless Christians are plagued by haunting feelings of shame. Joe gently unmasks your fears and reveals assurances from God's Word that will fill you with the peace and confidence before the Lord that you crave.

Becoming One: Emotionally, Spiritually & Sexually Can two uniquely individual people really become one--sexually, emotionally, and spiritually? Not only is it possible, it's what we were created for. It's what God had in mind all along. In this marriage-changing book, you'll learn how to nurture intimacy spouse at all levels.

Please visit www.joebeam.com to order the above books as well as additional books and resources.

Notes to Self

The most important things I've learned during this study that I WILL use for the rest of my life are...